EX(
PLA

by JULIA F. MORTON

Illustrated by
RICHARD E. YOUNGER
with assistance from
Sy and Dorothea Barlowe, Edith Singer, and Elmer Smith

Under the general editorship of
VERA R. WEBSTER

Original Project Editor: Herbert S. Zim

GOLDEN PRESS 🐾 NEW YORK
Western Publishing Company, Inc.

FOREWORD

"Exotic," literally, means "foreign," but it is today popularly applied to anything that is glamorous or exciting. It is used in a dual sense in this title. In most gardens, in any part of the world, the majority of the showy plants will be found to be truly "exotic," or foreign. This book presents nearly 400 plants of warm areas (tropical and subtropical) which are admired for the beauty of their flowers, foliage, or decorative fruits, and which are common enough to attract the eye of the layman—whether they are huge trees, shrubs, vines, cacti, or low-growing herbs. Plants that are strictly annuals and a temporary part of the landscape are omitted, as are most of those that are grown more for their edible fruit or other crop than as ornamentals.

In the text, cultural requirements are given when they help to explain the nature of a plant and its suitability for particular situations. Means of propagation are shown in the interest of the plant collector.

The artists, Richard Younger, Sy and Dorothea Barlowe, Elmer Smith, and Edith Singer have portrayed the striking features of each plant so as to arouse interest in its beauty, and aid identification when the reader and plant meet.

J.F.M.

Front cover illustrations	Back Cover
1. Passion Flower	1. Wild Plantain
2. Yellow Ixora	2. Yesterday, Today and Tomorrow
3. Gardenia	3. Pink Glory Bush
	4. Pomegranate

582.13
M889e

256838

CONTENTS

PARTS OF A COMPLETE FLOWER

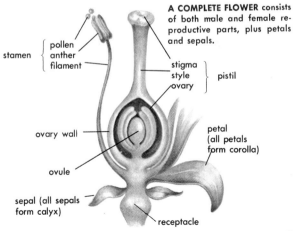

A COMPLETE FLOWER consists of both male and female reproductive parts, plus petals and sepals.

stamen
{ pollen
anther
filament

stigma
style
ovary } pistil

ovary wall

ovule

petal
(all petals
form corolla)

sepal (all sepals
form calyx)

receptacle

INTRODUCTION

The plant lover demands variety. To achieve it, he has moved plants from the wild to his garden, from his neighbor's garden to his own. He has sought plants from other countries and other continents. Plant introduction through government agencies has been motivated largely by economic reasons; but ornamental plants have not been neglected, for it is recognized that they play an important role in man's well-being—his material and spiritual enrichment and his recreation.

This book includes only plants that are subtropical or tropical and flourish out-of-doors all year only in warm areas (see list of Subtropical and Tropical areas, p. 6). Some of them are grown outside in the summer in cooler climates and many are cultivated as house plants or in greenhouses in all parts of the world.

WARM AREAS can be defined as the strip around the earth lying between the Tropic of Cancer and the Tropic of Capricorn, known as the tropical zone, and the parallel strips north and south of this band, known as the subtropical zones. Within these zones there is great variation in altitude and consequently in temperature. In the tropical zone, for example, there are mountains that are permanently covered with snow. Therefore, latitude alone does not determine climate.

ORNAMENTAL PLANTS, in the warm areas of the world, are a vital part of daily life and regional attractions throughout the year. And a great diversity of species is necessary to have an assortment in bloom in any given month and under varying soil and other conditions. In both subtropical and tropical areas, there are variations in amount and season of rainfall, and these factors of aridity or humidity have an important bearing on the selection of plants for certain regions.

A SUBTROPICAL AREA is one in which the average temperature of the coldest month is above 43°F and below 65°F.

ULTRA-TROPICAL PLANTS succumb wherever the average temperature of any month is below 65°F, and frost is likely to occur.

THE PLANT WORLD is divided into five primary divisions: algae; fungi; mosses and liverworts; ferns and fern allies; and flowering plants. The first four divisions are collectively known as non-flowering plants. The plants in this book all belong to the flowering plants and are arranged in the natural order of families in accordance with L. H. Bailey's *Manual of Cultivated Plants*. Brief descriptions are given of the major families. Within the family grouping, no rigid sequence is followed, except that when presenting more than one species in a genus, these are kept together.

THE COMMON NAME under which each plant is described is the one which appears to be most widely employed or which causes the least confusion with other plants. In some cases, alternate common names are given but space does not allow the listing of all colloquial names.

PLANT DESCRIPTIONS are deliberately limited to those details not represented in the illustrations. *Form* of leaf is not specified unless there is notable variation; *color* is not stated unless there is a range of colors. *Size* is not cited for all features but may be given for a leaf where leaves and flowers show the relative size of the latter. When leaves are compound, this information is given. Distinction is made between a calyx, bract, or sepal (see glossary, p. 9) and the true flower.

All plants vary in height because of inherent factors of age, environment, or cultural attention. A range is given to convey the approximate size.

THE BOTANICAL NAMES mainly correspond to those preferred in Bailey's *Manual* except where the renaming of certain species has been reported in *Baileya: Quarterly Journal of Horticultural Taxonomy* (Cornell Univ.) or elsewhere. No attempt is made to show the botanical synonyms.

FRUITS OR SEEDPODS OR SEEDS are mentioned where they constitute attractive or curious features of the plant; or are noteworthy as poisonous, edible, or particularly useful or undesirable in some other way; or when calling attention to their size or form may aid in the recognition of the plant.

SEASONS of flowering or fruiting cannot be stated precisely even for a limited area, since they fluctuate with prevailing weather. Even generalizing, using terms such as "summer" and "winter," can be misleading, for July and August occur in summer north of the equator and in winter south of the equator.

SUBTROPICAL AND TROPICAL AREAS AT LOW ELEVATIONS

Bahama Islands

Bermuda

Burma

Canary Islands

Central America

East Africa

East Indies

Florida

Gulf States (coastal strip)

Hawaiian Islands

India

Madagascar

Mediterranean Coast of Asia Minor

Mediterranean Coast of Europe

Mediterranean Coast of North Africa

Mexico

Northern South America

Polynesia and the South Pacific

Queensland and New South Wales, Australia

South Africa

Southeastern China

Southern California

Southern Japan

West Indies

West Tropical Africa

VARIATION IN CLIMATE WITH ALTITUDE WITHIN TROPICAL ZONES

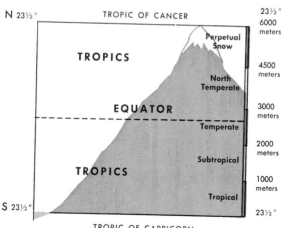

NOTE: Travelers should display all plant cuttings, seeds or other materials for quarantine inspection when entering any country, to avoid spreading of pests and diseases, or the introduction of any plant that might become a nuisance. An example of such a plant is the pretty but aggressive Brazilian Pepper (see p. 74) which has invaded vast tracts of Florida and Hawaii and causes skin and respiratory irritation.

BOTANICAL GARDENS

(from among the many featuring tropical and subtropical plants)

Botanic Gardens and National Herbarium, Melbourne, Australia

Brooklyn Botanic Garden, Brooklyn, N.Y.

Fairchild Tropical Garden, Miami, Fla.

Georgetown Botanic Gardens, Guyana

Honolulu Botanic Gardens, Honolulu

Hope Botanic Gardens, Mona, Jamaica

Jardim Botanico do Rio de Janeiro, Brazil

Longwood Gardens, Kennett Square, Pa.

Los Angeles State and County Arboretum, Arcadia, Calif.

Montreal Botanic Garden, Montreal, Canada

Munich Botanical Garden, Munich, Germany

Muséum National d'Histoire Naturelle, Paris

National Botanic Gardens, Lucknow, India

National Botanic Gardens of South Africa, Kirstenbosch

New York Botanical Garden, Bronx, N.Y.

Royal Botanic Gardens, Kew, England

Royal Botanic Gardens, Peradeniya, Ceylon

Royal Botanic Gardens, Port-of-Spain, Trinidad

University of California, Los Angeles—Arboretum

LIST OF PLANT FAMILIES

(Order follows L. H. Bailey, Manual of Cultivated Plants)

(*) Indicates major families which are briefly defined in text.

GLOSSARY

(Some botanical terms used in the text. See principal flower parts on sketch, page 3.)

Axillary: located in the upper angle between a leaf and the plant stem.

Bast: fiber located between the outer bark and the wood of a tree or shrub.

Bract, bractlet: a type of leaf, large or small, usually clustered with flowers and often resembling a petal.

Bulb: thickened part at base of plant stem; has several layers.

Bulbil: small bulb which has developed from parent bulb.

Calyx: a crown encircling the base of a flower.

Compound leaf: a leaf composed of two or more leaflets.

Corm: bulblike, but solid, base of plant stem, usually underground.

Deciduous: sheds leaves; opposite of evergreen.

Drupe: a fleshy fruit that does not split open; has a single seed in a stony shell.

Epiphyte: an air plant, roosting on another plant; not a parasite.

Herbaceous: not woody.

Inflorescence: flower cluster.

Legume: a pod that "splits open at both seams."

Lanceolate: lance-shaped.

Palmate: divided like a hand.

Pinnate: divided like a feather.

Pseudobulb: solid, thick part of orchid stem; above ground.

Rhizome: underground stem which creeps horizontally.

Rootstock: underground stem, shorter than a rhizome and more or less vertical.

Scarify: to scratch or make cuts in the surface.

Sepal: the divisions of a calyx.

Spadix: a fleshy spike covered with small, closely set flowers.

Spathe: a type of leaf, unlike a foliage leaf; protecting a flower cluster.

Subshrub: intermediate between a woody shrub and a non-woody plant.

Succulent: fleshy and thick.

Trifoliate: having leaves in whorls of three.

Trifoliolate: has three leaflets.

Tuber: a thickened, fleshy part at the base of a plant, usually underground, bearing buds, or "eyes," from which new plants develop.

Xerophytic: able to live with very little moisture.

palmate

pinnate

PALM FAMILY (Palmae) includes over 150 genera and nearly 3,000 species of the tropics and warm-temperate areas. Most are trees, with single or multiple trunks —smooth, rough, hairy or spiny; others are woody-stemmed shrubs or climbers. The leaves, unfolding from a terminal bud, are either featherlike or fanlike and some are immense. Flowers are small and clustered. Fruits often large or showy.

FISHTAIL PALM (*Caryota mitis*) is an ornamental East Indian palm (to 40 ft.) with many trunks. Leaves (4-9 ft. long) have fishtail-like leaflets (to 6 in. long). As each trunk ages, flowers and fruits are borne lower and lower until that trunk dies (in about 7 yrs.).

GOLDEN COCONUT (*Cocos nucifera*) is a showy variety from Malaya. It begins to bear when only a few feet high. As it is immune to the coconut nematode and "lethal yellowing," it is now in demand as an ornamental in Florida and West Indies.

MERRILL PALM (*Veitchia merrilli*), a pretty Philippine palm to 25 ft., has arched, pinnate leaves to 6 ft. long and striking fruits at odd seasons but especially at Christmas time. It is compact and increasingly popular in tropical landscaping.

ARUM FAMILY (Araceae) covers 107 genera and 1900 species, mostly tropical. All are herbs; some huge with stout, woody stems; some are vinelike with aerial roots that cling to supports or descend and take root in the soil. Most have tubers or thick rhizomes. The leaves may be simple or pinnately or palmately divided. Small flowers are usually massed on a cylindrical spadix shielded by a spathe, often colorful.

GIANT ARUM (*Amorphophallus titanum*), of Sumatra, is one of the marvels of the plant world. From its tuber (to 20 in. wide) springs a flower spike to 4 ft. tall, cupped by a fluted, foul-smelling spathe, and later a single leaf, to 15 ft. wide, on a stalk 6 to 10 ft. tall.

FANCY-LEAVED CALADIUM (*Caladium bicolor*) is a tuberous tropical American plant to 2 ft. high, with succulent stems supporting thin, silky leaves (to 1 ft. long), which die back in winter. There are hundreds of varieties. Vivid in full sun.

CERIMAN (*Monstera deliciosa*), from Mexico and Central America, is a sprawling or climbing plant with thick stems and perforated leaves (to 3 ft.). The spike of tiny flowers becomes a compound, edible fruit. Easily grown from cuttings in pots indoors or outside in warm areas; prefers shade and damp soil.

DUMB CANE (*Dieffenbachia maculata*), from Brazil, is an erect plant (to 8 ft.) with a fleshy stem and leaves blotched with white, yellow, or pale green. A popular house plant, it is grown outdoors in warm areas in shade or sun, sheltered from strong winds. Cuttings root quickly. The juice is poisonous.

FLAMINGO FLOWER (*Anthurium andreanum*), native to Colombia, is a short-stemmed plant (to 3 ft.) with glossy leaves (10-12 in. long. Its yellow, white or pink spike of tiny flowers rises from a waxy spathe—red, pink, orange, white or green. Grown from seeds or division in subdued light and moist atmosphere.

HUNTER'S ROBE (*Rhaphidophora aurea*), native to the Solomon Islands, is a large vine with aerial roots. Leaves from 6 in. long, when grown in pots or as ground cover, to 18 in. when climbing trees. Old leaves deeply and irregularly divided. Grown from cuttings; prefers light shade and rich soil. Rarely blooms. Formerly *Pothos* (or *Scindapsus*) *aureus*.

PINEAPPLE FAMILY (Bromeliaceae) includes 50 or 60 genera and more than 1,300 species of tropical America and the West Indies. The typical form is a rosette of more or less spiny, straplike leaves, green or variegated. Borne in a rigid spike or loose, drooping cluster, the flowers and/or bracts may be colorful. Most bromeliads are epiphytic and need much moisture; some are terrestrial and prefer aridity.

PITCAIRNIA (*Pitcairnia maidifolia*), occurring wild in Costa Rica, Colombia, and Venezuela, is a terrestrial bromeliad to 5 ft. tall with spineless leaves to 5 ft. long and 2½ in. wide. Flowers, massed in a 12-in. spike on a stalk 3 to 4 ft. long, have white petals flanked by red or purplish bracts.

AECHMEA (*Aechmea chantinii*), an epiphyte from Brazil, has stiff, faintly toothed leaves (to 1 ft. long and 2 in. wide). Showy red or mauve leaf-bracts are borne below the branched red-and-yellow flower spike (4 to 6 in. long on 12-in. stalk). Propagated by suckers. Needs full light, very little soil.

BILLBERGIA (*Billbergia venezuelana*), an epiphyte (to 3 ft.), is found on tall trees in hot lowlands of Venezuela. Leaves are stiff and toothed. The drooping inflorescence, most colorful in the sun, is the gaudiest in the genus. As with other species, the showy flowers and bracts last only a few days. Propagated by seed or offsets. Funnel must be kept full of water.

DYCKIA *(Dyckia altissima)* is a terrestrial bromeliad (to 1½ ft.) forming clumps on dry plains of northern Argentina. Its leaves are rigid and waxy, the branched inflorescence 2½ to 3 ft. tall. Propagated by suckers. Good drainage essential.

FLAMING VRIESIA *(Vriesia splendens)*, from Guyana, is an epiphyte (to 3 ft.) with smooth, leathery leaves (to 15 in. long), yellow flowers, and red bracts. Grown from offsets and seeds in semi-shade. Var. *major* is called Flaming Sword.

PORTEA *(Portea petropolitana)*, an epiphyte from the coast of southeastern Brazil, occurs in several forms in the wild; has spiny-edged leaves. The flower spikes may be salmon and lavender or green and purple. Var. *extensa* has a coral stalk.

TILLANDSIA *(Tillandsia cyanea)* is native to Ecuador, Guatemala, and Costa Rica. It is an epiphyte (to 2½ ft.) but can be grown in pots with daily sprinkling. Needs full sun. Propagated by seed or, preferably, small offsets in spring.

LILY FAMILY (Liliaceae) embraces more than 200-250 genera and 2,000 species of temperate and tropical climates. They are mainly perennial herbs with bulbs, corms or fleshy rootstocks. Only a few are treelike. The flowers have 6 lobes or segments, 6 or 3 stamens and a 3-celled, superior ovary, the latter distinguishing the *Lily* from the *Amaryllis* family. These two families usually share between them the 500-odd species sometimes placed in the *Agave* family (Agavaceae). Most liliaceous plants are showy ornamentals.

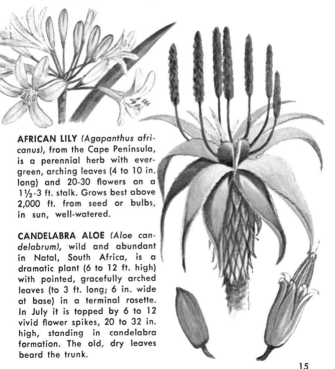

AFRICAN LILY (Agapanthus africanus), from the Cape Peninsula, is a perennial herb with evergreen, arching leaves (4 to 10 in. long) and 20-30 flowers on a 1½-3 ft. stalk. Grows best above 2,000 ft. from seed or bulbs, in sun, well-watered.

CANDELABRA ALOE (Aloe candelabrum), wild and abundant in Natal, South Africa, is a dramatic plant (6 to 12 ft. high) with pointed, gracefully arched leaves (to 3 ft. long; 6 in. wide at base) in a terminal rosette. In July it is topped by 6 to 12 vivid flower spikes, 20 to 32 in. high, standing in candelabra formation. The old, dry leaves beard the trunk.

15

GLORY LILY *(Gloriosa superba)*, from tropical Africa and Asia, is a slender, climbing lily (to 10 ft.) with tendrils at its leaf-tips. It dies after flowering, the next shoot coming up at a different point as the tuber (which is very toxic) elongates underground. Needs full sun.

CHILE BELLS *(Lapageria rosea)*, a vinelike shrub (to 20 ft.) from Chile, has wiry, twining stems and leathery leaves (2 to 3½ in. long). Popular in California and in greenhouses for its blossoms in spring. Grown from seeds or layers. Needs shade and moisture.

TI (pronounced "tee") *(Cordyline terminalis)*, native from Australia to Hawaii, is a slender shrub (to 12 ft.). Leaves (to 2 ft. long) occur in various shades of red, pink, purple or green; some may be white-striped. Grown from cuttings or seeds in sun or semi-shade. Root edible; fresh leaves used for hula skirts and food wrapping.

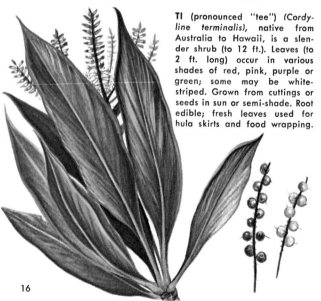

TORCH LILY *(Kniphofia uvaria)*, of South Africa, is common in California gardens and has gone wild in Central America. From clumps of leaves (to 3 ft. long) arise stalks (4 to 9 ft.), bearing brilliant spikes in summer and fall. The several varieties and hybrids are propagated by division, offsets, or seeds. Provide full sun, much moisture.

OUR LORD'S CANDLE *(Yucca whipplei)*, one of the most striking and beautiful features of the Coast-range vegetation of southern California, has been prized in European gardens for over 100 years. From the underground stem arises a clump (to 6 ft. wide) of sharp-tipped, saw-edged leaves (8 to 30 in. long) and an immense columnar flower cluster (8 to 15 ft.).

17

AMARYLLIS FAMILY (Amaryllidaceae) contains 90 genera and some 1,200 species, mainly of South Africa, South America, and Mediterranean area. They are perennial herbs, mostly of arid land, with large bulbs, fibrous roots or rhizomes. The flowers emerge from a spathelike bract atop a central stalk and have 6 segments (3 inner ones, petals; outer 3, sepals). Ovary usually inferior. Many are prized ornamentals.

MILK-AND-WINE LILY (*Crinum augustum*), from Mauritius and the Seychelles, has a bulb to 6 in. thick from which rises 2- to 3-ft. leaves and a stalk that bends to the ground with the weight of 12 to 30 flowers. Does not seed. Forms offsets slowly.

GUERNSEY LILY (*Nerine sarniensis*), of South Africa, is popular in California. The flower stalk (2-2½ ft.) appears in fall, followed by flat leaves (to 12 in. long). There are several varieties—white, pink or crimson. Grown from offsets.

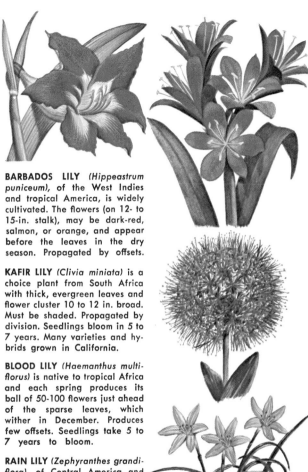

BARBADOS LILY *(Hippeastrum puniceum)*, of the West Indies and tropical America, is widely cultivated. The flowers (on 12- to 15-in. stalk), may be dark-red, salmon, or orange, and appear before the leaves in the dry season. Propagated by offsets.

KAFIR LILY *(Clivia miniata)* is a choice plant from South Africa with thick, evergreen leaves and flower cluster 10 to 12 in. broad. Must be shaded. Propagated by division. Seedlings bloom in 5 to 7 years. Many varieties and hybrids grown in California.

BLOOD LILY *(Haemanthus multiflorus)* is native to tropical Africa and each spring produces its ball of 50-100 flowers just ahead of the sparse leaves, which wither in December. Produces few offsets. Seedlings take 5 to 7 years to bloom.

RAIN LILY *(Zephyranthes grandiflora)*, of Central America and the West Indies, springs up in summer rains from 1-in. bulbs. Flowers, often preceding leaves, are long lasting. Popular in borders, in sun or semi-shade.

19

HURRICANE LILY *(Lycoris aurea)*, from China, sends up flowers on a 2-ft. stalk during hurricane season (Aug.-Oct.). Leaves (to 1 ft. long) follow and last all winter. The 2-in. bulb may be cut into sections for planting 8-10 in. apart. Multiplies fast in semi-shade.

CENTURY PLANT *(Agave americana)*, of tropical America, is naturalized in Europe, Africa and East Indies. Its spine-edged leaves reach 6 ft. In 10 or 15 years, it may send up a flower stalk (25 to 40 ft.) and then die. Grown from suckers.

TUBEROSE *(Polianthes tuberosa)*, a Mexican plant popular in warm regions, has grassy leaves (to 1½ ft. long) and very fragrant blooms (on 3½ ft. stalk) in summer and fall. They are often sold as cut flowers. The plant dies back in winter.

AMAZON LILY *(Eucharis grandiflora)*, a native of Colombia, has a 2-in. bulb and evergreen leaves (8 to 12 in. long) and produces in late winter a flower stalk (1 to 2 ft.) with 3 to 6 lovely, mildly fragrant flowers. Grown from offsets, protected from full sun.

JACOBEAN LILY *(Sprekelia formosissima)*, from Mexico, has been widely cultivated for 300 years. Leaves may accompany or follow the single, brilliant flower borne on a 1-ft. stalk. Even in warm areas, the 2-in. bulb is usually taken up for a rest to force regular blooming.

TACCA FAMILY (Taccaceae)

BAT FLOWER *(Tacca chantrieri)*, from Malaya, has a creeping rootstock and glossy leaves (1½ ft. long) which appear in spring and wither in fall. The bizarre flowers (on 3-ft. stalk) are accompanied by leafy bracts and threadlike bractlets. Grown from seed or root-division in shade with plenty of moisture.

IRIS FAMILY (Iridaceae)

1. TIGER FLOWER (*Tigridia pavonia*) is one of the most glamorous plants of Mexico and Guatemala where it is abundant in cornfields. Widely cultivated and admired, it was grown in Europe as early as the 16th Century. In the rainy season, the bulb (to 1½ in. wide) puts forth erect stems (to 2½ ft.) bearing a few stiff leaves and continuous blooms (3 to 6 in. wide). Individual flowers—red, yellow, violet or white, with contrasting spots—open early in the morning and fade in the afternoon, but fresh ones are always present for 2 to 3 months. Propagated by offsets, or seeds which produce flowers in 1 yr. Needs sun and well-drained soil. Aztecs ate the nutlike bulb.

2. BLACKBERRY LILY (*Belamcanda chinensis*), from China and Japan, is a perennial herb (2 to 5 ft.) with a creeping rootstock. Blooms in summer. Propagated by division. The flowers and open pods showing the glossy seeds are frequently used in arrangements.

3. PEACOCK IRIS (*Moraea pavonia*), a South African herb (1-2 ft. high) has hairy leaves and a succession of flowers, each lasting only a day. Common form is scarlet with a dark-green or blue-black spot; others are white with blue spot, purple with blue-black spot, or plain yellow. Propagated by division. Needs full sun and fairly dry, light soil. Resembles true iris.

4. MARICA (*Neomarica caerulea*) is a perennial herb (to 2½ ft.) from southern Brazil with short, creeping rootstock and leathery leaves (3-6 ft. long). The handsome flowers (in summer) may be blue or lilac, barred with brown, yellow, orange or white. Propagated by root-division. Needs rich soil and much moisture.

5. BUGLE LILY (*Watsonia meriana*), wild on the coast of South Africa and the leading *Watsonia* in cultivation, is a gladiolus-like plant with stiff leaves (to 20 in.). The 3-4 ft. flower stalk bears 12-20 flowers—red, salmon or pinkish—in spring. Grown from seeds or offsets in sandy soil. Needs water and sun.

6. BABOON-ROOT (*Babiana stricta*), from the Cape Peninsula, is a hairy plant (8-16 in. high). The flowers (in spring), mildly sweet-scented, may be blue, purple, red or yellow. Grown from offsets or seed in light shade and transplanted yearly. Baboons eat the corms.

7. WALKING IRIS (*Trimeza martinicensis*), from tropical America and the West Indies, has a fan-like clump of leaves (2-3 ft. tall) and slim flower stalk (1-3 ft. high). Blooms summer to fall. New plantlets are borne on old stalks which bend to the ground so that they may root. Propagated by seed or division. Not particular as to soil. Does well in sun or partial shade.

BANANA FAMILY (Musaceae) is made up of 5 or 6 genera and about 125 species of large-leaved tropical herbs. Some are treelike; few have woody stems.

PINK VELVET BANANA (*Musa velutina*), from Assam, is a charming miniature, pink-stemmed banana plant (3 to 6 ft.) with upright flower cluster and velvety fruits that split open when ripe. Grown from seeds or suckers in part shade. The seeds are used in edible-banana breeding. There are ornamental hybrids between this species and *M. flaviflora*.

BIRD-OF-PARADISE (*Strelitzia reginae*), native to South Africa, is a large herb with a fanlike clump of long-stalked, blue-green leaves (to 5 ft. tall) and an outstanding inflorescence suggesting a brilliant bird in flight. Propagated by division or seeds. Seedlings may not bloom for 7 yrs. Slow-growing, does best in full sun, with rich soil and abundant moisture.

LOBSTER CLAW (long known as *Heliconia humilis*, now *Heliconia* sp. 1) is native to South America and widely cultivated. It forms a clump of erect, long-stalked leaves (to 6 or 8 ft. tall) and in early summer bears an upright spike of vivid, clawlike bracts which enclose the small flowers. Propagated by division. Needs abundant moisture in full sun or semi-shade. The spikes are often cut for decoration.

WILD PLANTAIN (*Heliconia wagneriana*), native from Mexico to Brazil, is commonly grown in the West Indies and tropical areas of the Old World. It is a stout plant (6-12 ft. or more) with bananalike leaves (2-5 ft.). The inflorescence is short-stalked, erect and showy for several months. Blue-coated seeds rarely planted. Suckers form large clumps on moist land, in sun or part-shade. Formerly called *H. bihai*, syn. *H. elongata*.

HANGING HELICONIA (*Heliconia collinsiana*), native to the lowlands of Guatemala, El Salvador and British Honduras, reaches 8 to 15 ft. The leaves are usually whitish on the lower side and the gay inflorescence (to 1½ ft.) dangles upside-down, the light-yellow flowers protruding from the bracts. Salt and foods brought to native markets are wrapped in the leaves, and the inflorescences are sold for decorating churches, particularly at Christmas time. Another species with spectacular hanging cluster is *H. rostrata*.

GINGER FAMILY (Zingiberaceae) covers 45 genera and nearly 800 species from tropical Asia and Africa. These pungent, perennial herbs have fleshy rhizomes or tuberous roots, erect, canelike stems, and entire leaves, mainly lance-shaped or oblong. The flowers, in terminal heads, spikes or hanging clusters, are tubular, 3-parted, and often large and showy. Gingers grow readily on moist soil and tend to clump.

RED GINGER (*Alpinia purpurata*), from the South Pacific islands, forms a clump of leafy stems (4 to 15 ft. tall) tipped with spikes (6 to 12 in.) of thick, red bracts shielding the slim, tubular flowers. Young plantlets develop in the spikes.

SHELL GINGER (*Alpinia speciosa*) is an Asiatic plant with 6- to 12-ft. leafy stems, bearing in spring and summer drooping clusters of pearly buds and open, seashell-like flowers (to 2 in. long). The clumps, lush in semi-shade, need thinning.

TORCH GINGER (*Nicolai elatior*), from the East Indies, has arching stems (to 15-20 ft.) and 3- to 5-ft. stalks topped by elegant cones (to 10 in. wide) of waxy, red or pink bracts from which a few, small flowers peer. Formerly, *Phaeomeria magnifica*.

WHITE GINGER (*Hedychium coronarium*), native to India and Malaya, forms spreading clumps (6-7 ft. tall) and in summer has terminal spikes of sweet-scented blossoms (to 3½ in. wide). Great numbers are used in leis and in perfume making in Hawaii.

YELLOW GINGER (*Hedychium flavum*), from India, has 3- to 5-ft. stems tipped with clusters of fragrant flowers (to 3 in. wide). Not as popular as white ginger for leis, but their oil is more widely used in the perfume trade for exotic scents.

CRAPE GINGER (*Costus speciosus*), native to southern Asia and the Philippines, has leaves (hairy beneath) spirally set on stems 4 to 10 ft. tall. From spikes of red bracts emerge odd flowers: the white portion of each is a funnel-like stamen.

PEACOCK PLANT (*Kaempferia roscoeana*), from Burma, is a stemless plant with a fleshy rhizome and two, thick, horizontal, satiny leaves (about 4 in. long), iridescent above, purplish-red and hairy beneath. Blooms continuously in summer.

CANNA FAMILY
(Cannaceae)

INDIAN SHOT (*Canna indica*), native to tropical America (not India), has slender stems (3 to 5 ft.) and is widely grown and naturalized in the tropics and southern United States. The hard seeds are used for shot, necklaces and Buddhist rosaries.

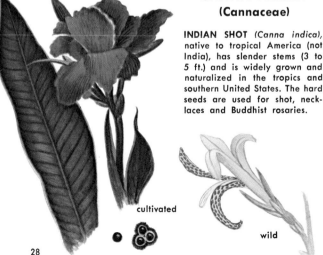

cultivated

wild

ORCHID FAMILY (Orchidaceae)

The orchid family embraces more than 600 genera and 20,000 species of perennial herbs, abounding in the tropics where they are mostly epiphytic. Temperate species are usually terrestrial. The epiphytic types have aerial roots that cling to their hosts and absorbing roots that take up moisture. Most develop pseudobulbs or fleshy leaves in which water and reserve nourishment are stored. The plants range from minute leafless forms to large specimens several feet in height. Some (monopodial) progressively elongate from a terminal bud; others (sympodial) put out a succession of axillary shoots. The leaves, commonly more or less fleshy or rubbery, may be narrow, oblong, oval, or rounded. The flowers may be tiny or up to 9 in. across, borne singly or in massive sprays. Some are fragrant, especially at certain times; others scentless. Natural species and hybrids occur in many hues and combinations of colors. Orchids are aristocrats among cultivated flowering plants, and are almost exclusively esthetic in appeal (except for vanilla orchid and others yielding salep). Orchids are propagated by division, offsets, cuttings, or seeds. The latter, fine as powder, are produced in great numbers and, in the wild, are sown by the wind. In captivity, seeds are germinated on nutrient-agar in glass flasks and the seedlings transplanted to pots. Orchids are usually grown in osmunda (fibrous roots of *Osmunda* fern), Douglas fir bark, or on slabs of tree fern trunk, and they flourish in a moist atmosphere. On pages 30 and 31 are the important genera. Many more are illustrated and described in the Golden Nature Guide *Orchids*.

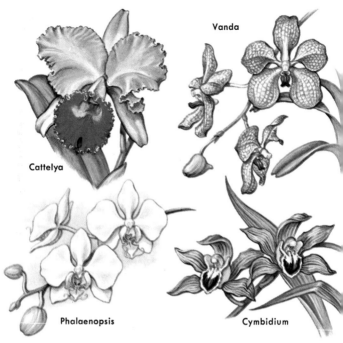

Vanda

Cattelya

Phalaenopsis

Cymbidium

CATTLEYA orchids from tropical America are most popular. A favorite with home growers is C. *trianaei*, often with 100 blooms (to 7 in. wide). There are thousands of *Cattleya* hybrids, between the various species and also with closely related genera.

PHALAENOPSIS (moth orchids) are found in tropical Asia and the East Indies. They have leafy stems, broad, leathery leaves (mostly 6-12 in. long, some 2-3 ft.); no pseudobulbs. Flowers, in drooping sprays, are often white tinged with rose or lilac.

VANDA species range from India to New Guinea. They are epiphytic and sun-loving, without pseudobulbs; have leafy stems, short or reaching to 7 ft. Leaves strap-shaped or, rarely, rounded and fleshy. Flowers fragrant, in clusters of 3 to 80.

CYMBIDIUM orchids (mostly epiphytes) are from the Far East. Usually with pseudobulbs, they have narrow, grasslike leaves to 3 ft. long. Flowers are generally large and showy in tall, arching sprays which last from 6 weeks to 3 months.

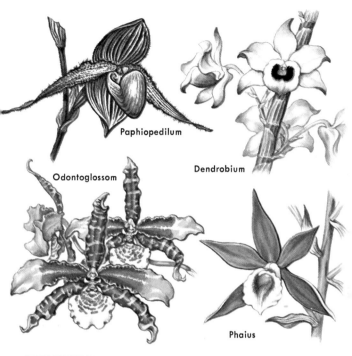

Paphiopedilum

Dendrobium

Odontoglossom

Phaius

PAPHIOPEDILUM orchids (from tropical Asia) and *Phragmipedium* (tropical American) are either terrestrial or epiphytic. They are the so-called "cypripedium" (lady-slipper) orchids of greenhouses. True *Cypripedium* species are not tropical.

ODONTOGLOSSOM orchids are from the highlands of tropical America. They are epiphytic, have short rhizomes and short, broad pseudobulbs bearing 1 to 3 leaves. From their bases arise the crested-lipped flowers (to 6 in. wide) in slender sprays.

DENDROBIUM species are epiphytic, primarily Malayan. Their stem-like pseudobulbs are usually elongated, with short, fleshy leaves. Flowers (to 5 in. wide) are in short spikes or drooping sprays. Some lose their leaves before or during blooming.

PHAIUS genus (epiphytic or terrestrial) is from tropical Africa, Madagascar, Asia, Australia and Pacific islands. The renowned nun's orchid (shown) has plump pseudobulbs, leaves to 3 ft., flower spike to 4 ft. with 12 to 18 flowers to 4 in. wide.

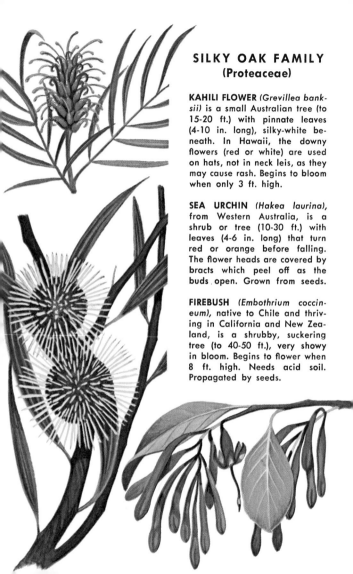

SILKY OAK FAMILY
(Proteaceae)

KAHILI FLOWER *(Grevillea banksii)* is a small Australian tree (to 15-20 ft.) with pinnate leaves (4-10 in. long), silky-white beneath. In Hawaii, the downy flowers (red or white) are used on hats, not in neck leis, as they may cause rash. Begins to bloom when only 3 ft. high.

SEA URCHIN *(Hakea laurina)*, from Western Australia, is a shrub or tree (10-30 ft.) with leaves (4-6 in. long) that turn red or orange before falling. The flower heads are covered by bracts which peel off as the buds open. Grown from seeds.

FIREBUSH *(Embothrium coccineum)*, native to Chile and thriving in California and New Zealand, is a shrubby, suckering tree (to 40-50 ft.), very showy in bloom. Begins to flower when 8 ft. high. Needs acid soil. Propagated by seeds.

SPIKY HONEYSUCKLE (*Banksia ericifolia*), from New South Wales is a small, spreading tree or shrub (to 15 or 20 ft.), its dense foliage silvery beneath. Flowers (yellow, gold, or russet) long-lasting in bouquets; full of nectar sought by birds.

SCARLET HONEYSUCKLE (*Banksia coccinea*), native to Western Australia, is a shrub to 12 ft. with stiff, spiny foliage and abundant flowers in spring. *Banksia* cones are heated to free the seeds or laid between wet pads until seeds germinate.

KING PROTEA (*Protea cynaroides*), of South Africa, is a bush (to 6 ft.) with leathery leaves and flower heads (8-12 in. wide) called "honey pots" as the copious sweet nectar is made into sugar. Grown from seed in full sun. Blooms in 4-5 years.

SUGAR BUSH (*Protea mellifera*), common on low mountain slopes of South Africa and long in cultivation, is a shrub or small tree (7-10 ft.) with red, pink or white flower heads (to 5½ in. high). The concentrated nectar ("bush syrup") is a local cough remedy.

WARATAH (*Telopea speciosissima*), of New South Wales, is an erect shrub (to 10-12 ft.) with stiff, evergreen leaves and gorgeous flower heads (3-4 in. wide) that last 2 weeks in vases. Seedlings may bloom in 2 years. Difficult to grow in pots.

FIREWHEEL TREE (*Stenocarpus sinuatus*), an Australian tree (from 30-100 ft.), has variable leaves, pinnately lobed (1-1½ ft. long) or unlobed (6-10 in. long), and is spectacular in bloom. Grown from seed; begins to flower when very young.

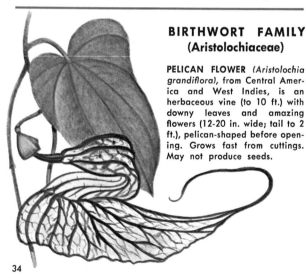

BIRTHWORT FAMILY
(Aristolochiaceae)

PELICAN FLOWER (*Aristolochia grandiflora*), from Central America and West Indies, is an herbaceous vine (to 10 ft.) with downy leaves and amazing flowers (12-20 in. wide; tail to 2 ft.), pelican-shaped before opening. Grows fast from cuttings. May not produce seeds.

CORAL VINE (*Antigonon leptopus*), a native of Mexico, naturalized in southern Texas, California, and Florida, is widely cultivated. It is a slim vine, climbing (to 20-40 ft.) by means of tendrils at the tips of the flower clusters. It blooms from spring to fall or later. Best grown by dividing tubers.

SANGRE DE TORO (*Ruprechtia coriacea*), from northern South America, is a slender tree (to 20 ft.) with 3-in. leaves and inconspicuous flowers (male and female on separate trees). The female develop into seeds with rosy-red wings, borne in dense clusters in midwinter in Florida. Propagated by air-layering.

LONG JOHN (*Triplaris melaenodendron*), from Central America, is a very slender, soft-wooded tree (30-65 ft.) with pale, smooth, flaking bark, short branches, and downy leaves (7-16 in. long). Male trees are not showy but the female produce masses of colorful flowerlike fruits in spring. Stinging ants live in hollow branches.

FOUR O'CLOCK FAMILY (Nyctaginaceae)

BOUGAINVILLEA is a genus of Brazilian climbing shrubs with evergreen leaves (to 4 in.), prized for their handsome clusters of papery bracts (in 3's) which enclose the small, white flowers. *B. spectabilis* is tall-growing (to 25 ft.) with downy stems and hooked spines, and bracts of various shades of red and orange and sometimes white. *B. glabra* is more compact, has purple or crimson bracts, can be pruned and grown as a shrub or pot plant. The leaves of one variety are variegated with white. Bougainvilleas are grown from cuttings.

FOUR O'CLOCK (*Mirabilis jalapa*), from tropical America, is a perennial herb (to 3-4 ft.) with a thick tuber and smooth leaves (2-6 in. long). The flowers open in late afternoon; are bright-magenta, yellow or white. The black seeds contain a white, starchy substance formerly used as face powder in the Orient. Grown from seed, in sun.

CARPETWEED FAMILY (Aizoaceae)

SOUR FIG *(Carpobrotus acinaciforme)*, native to sandy coasts of Cape Province, South Africa, is a succulent plant with long, thick, trailing stems and thick, 3-angled leaves (1½-3½ in. long), joined in pairs. Flowers (to 5 in. wide) are largest of all so-called "fig marigolds" (formerly grouped in genus *Mesembryanthemum*, now divided into over 100 genera including *Carpobrotus*, *Lampranthus*, and *Drosanthemum*). All grown from cuttings in full sun. Withstand salt spray.

DEWFLOWER *(Drosanthemum floribundum)*, found in brackish soil on Paarden Island, Cape Province, has threadlike branches and is low-creeping when young but rather woody and up to 5 in. high when old. Leaves cylindrical, ½ to ⅝ in. long; 1 in. thick. Flowers form a dense carpet of color in May and June in California. The plant is a good soil retainer. Has high resistance to wind and salt spray.

PINK FIG MARIGOLD *(Lampranthus glomeratus)*, from South Africa, is popular in Bermuda and Hawaii. Its thin stems may be erect (to 2 ft.) or hug the ground. The leaves are slim and 3-angled. Blooms for several months. In Hawaii, leis are made of the buds which open after stringing, and the flowers last for days. Grown from seed and cuttings; needs some shade and moisture in hot weather.

S

S

S

WATER LILY FAMILY (Nymphaceae)

CAPE BLUE WATER LILY *(Nymphaea capensis)*, from South and East Africa, has almost circular leaves (12-16 in. wide), dark green or brown. The violet-scented flowers (6-8 in.) open 4 days from morning to late afternoon. Var. *zanzibariensis* has larger, darker blooms.

RED BENGAL WATER LILY *(Nymphaea rubra)*, from India, has nearly round leaves (12-18 in. wide), deeply toothed, maroon at first, later greenish; downy below. Flowers open 3 or 4 nights and close about noon. Many varieties; also hybrids between this and other species.

ROYAL WATER LILY *(Victoria amazonica)*, from Guyana, is the largest of all aquatic plants. Its floating leaves (3-7½ ft. wide) are reddish and prickly beneath. Flowers open late in day, turn from white to rose. Variety *Randii* has dark-red blooms. Grown from 2-yr.-old seeds. Widely known as *V. regia*.

MAGNOLIA FAMILY
(Magnoliaceae)

MAGNOLIA (*Magnolia grandiflora*), of the southern United States, succeeds in Florida and West Indies and above 3,000 ft. in ultra-tropical areas. Is a stately evergreen (to 100 ft.) grown from seeds, layers and cuttings.

CUSTARD APPLE FAMILY (Annonaceae)

ILANG-ILANG (*Cananga odorata*), native to the East Indies, is a slim, evergreen tree (to 80 or 100 ft.). Blooms all year. The rich-scented flowers (to 3½ in. long) yield oil for fine perfume and are used in leis. Tree develops rapidly from seeds.

CALABASH NUTMEG (*Monodora myristica*), from tropical West Africa, is a deciduous tree (20-80 ft.) with shining leaves, fragrant flowers, and black pod (8-12 in. long, 6 in. wide) containing nutmeg-flavored seeds used for spice and necklaces.

POPPY FAMILY (Papaveraceae)

PRICKLY POPPY (*Argemone mexicana*), a native of tropical America which has spread to all warm areas, is a spiny herb (2-3 ft. high), showy both as a weed and as a garden ornamental. Often depicted in art. Flowers may be white or yellow.

PLUME POPPY (*Macleaya cordata*), from China and Japan, is an herbaceous perennial (to 5-8 ft.) with creeping rootstock and handsome leaves (to 8 in. wide), white on the underside. Flower sprays reach 1 ft. in length. Grown from suckers or cuttings.

MATILIJA POPPY (*Romneya coulteri*), native to Mexico and southern California, is a bushy, suckering plant (3-8 ft. high) with showy and fragrant flowers (3-6 in. wide). Propagated by division; seedlings slow to bloom. Thrives in full sun.

CAPER FAMILY (Capparidaceae)

SPIDERFLOWER (Cleome spinosa), native to tropical America and widely naturalized, is a pungent, odorous herb (to 3-4 ft.) with spiny stems and compound leaves. Seedpods long and slim. Seeds sprout easily. Likes full sun and moist soil. Excellent honeybee plant.

BARNA (Crateva roxburghii), native to India, Malaya and Central Africa, is a deciduous tree (to 50-100 ft.) with trifoliate leaves, very showy in bloom. The flowers (in clusters 4-12 in. long, 10 in. wide) have a garlic odor. Grown from seeds; in sun. Leaves may inflame skin.

MORINGA FAMILY (Moringaceae)

HORSERADISH TREE (Moringa oleifera), from northern India, is a graceful tree (to 25 ft.) with thrice-pinnate leaves (9-24 in. long) and copious flowers and fruits all year. The roots are prepared like horseradish; the young pods, leaves and seeds are eaten. The latter yield ben oil, valued for culinary use and in cosmetics. Grown from seeds or cuttings.

ORPINE FAMILY (Crassulaceae) consists of 33 genera and 1,500 species of temperate and tropical regions. Most are perennial succulent herbs or subshrubs with fleshy stems and leaves, the latter waxy, often in rosettes, sometimes colorful. Flowers may be showy. Ideal for rock gardens; arid situations.

SCARLET PAINTBRUSH (*Crassula falcata*), native to the Cape Province, South Africa, and widely cultivated is a semi-shrub (to 3 ft.) with a fleshy stem and very fleshy leaves (3-4 in. long). The flowers (bright-scarlet, orange or sometimes white) are in dense, flat terminal clusters. Grown from cuttings, leaf cuttings or seed. Needs perfect drainage.

ICE ROSE (*Echeveria glauca*), from Mexico, is a stemless, compact, saucer-shaped rosette (to 4 in. wide) with thin, rounded leaves. Flower stalk (8-12 in. tall) bears clusters of 8-20 flowers. Easily grown from offsets; forms dense beds.

MEXICAN SNOWBALL (*Echeveria elegans*), from Hidalgo, is stemless and has tight rosettes of 2-in. leaves. Flower stalks (4-10 in. tall) bear clusters of 5-10 blooms. Var. *simulans* has red-tipped leaves and reddish-yellow flowers. Grown by offsets.

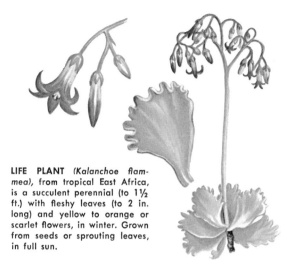

LIFE PLANT *(Kalanchoe flammea)*, from tropical East Africa, is a succulent perennial (to 1½ ft.) with fleshy leaves (to 2 in. long) and yellow to orange or scarlet flowers, in winter. Grown from seeds or sprouting leaves, in full sun.

PIG'S EAR *(Cotyledon undulata)*, from the Cape Province, Africa, is a shrubby plant (to 3 ft.), its leaves (3-5 in. long) coated with a mealy, white or silvery bloom. Flowers are orange or red. Cuttings of old stems will put out new shoots.

GUMMY AEONIUM *(Aeonium glutinosum)*, native to Madeira, has an erect or prostrate stem, very sticky, as are the 3- to 4-in. leaves. The flower cluster (1 ft. long and wide) is borne on a 2-ft., leafy stalk. Leaves used to harden fishing lines.

PITTOSPORUM FAMILY (Pittosporaceae)

TASMANIAN CHRISTMAS BUSH (*Bursaria spinosa*), found throughout Australia and Tasmania, is a shrub (to 15 ft.) or small tree (to 20-30 ft.), with small, spiny leaves. Terminal spikes (5-6 in. tall) of sweetly scented flowers are produced in abundance in summer (late December in its native home). The red seedpods which follow are also ornamental. Grown from cuttings.

VICTORIAN LAUREL (*Pittosporum undulatum*), from the warm parts of Australia and Tasmania, is a beautiful, low-branching tree (to 20-40 ft.). The leaves (4-6 in. long) are laurel-like, wavy and shining. Fragrant flowers are succeeded by decorative fruits which split open when ripe. The tree is quick-growing from seed. It is wind-resistant, salt-tolerant, and may be grown as a clipped hedge. A popular variety has variegated leaves.

PITCHBERRY (*Pittosporum heterophyllum*), native to China, is a spreading, drooping or semi-reclining shrub (3-6 ft. high, or up to 12 ft. if given support). The leaves (1-3½ in. long) are variable in form; the flowers very fragrant. The clusters of small, black berries stand out because of the light green of the foliage. Very slow-growing; tolerant of poor, dry soil; highly drought-resistant. Excellent plant for embankments and rock gardens.

CUNONIA FAMILY (Cunoniaceae)

NEW SOUTH WALES CHRISTMAS BUSH (*Ceratopetalum gummiferum*), an elegant shrub or small tree (to 30 ft. or more), is the most commonly cultivated native plant of New South Wales. Although the flowers are small and unappealing in scent, their mature calyces are red and spectacular in late December when cut sprays are popular for decoration. Grown from seeds or cuttings.

SWEETSHADE (*Hymenosporum flavum*), from subtropical Australia, may be either a broad shrub or narrow tree (to 25 or 50 ft.). The evergreen leaves (3 to 6 in. long) are downy on the underside. Very fragrant, attractive flowers are displayed in loose terminal clusters (4-8 in. wide) and are succeeded by thick capsules (1 in. long) containing many winged seeds. Grown from seeds or cuttings.

ROSE FAMILY (Rosaceae) is composed of some 115 genera and 3,200 species, primarily of temperate climates. They range from low herbs to shrubs (some climbing) and small trees, and may be thorny. The leaves are alternate, compound or simple. A typical flower has 4 or 5 petals (usually white, pink or red) surrounding a tuft of stamens. Seeds may be borne outside or inside a fleshy receptacle commonly called a fruit, which is usually edible and often ornamental. Roses (Rosa species) are grown in the subtropics and tropics but are better suited to colder regions.

SILVERLEAF COTONEASTER (*Cotoneaster pannosa*), from southwest China, is popular in California and Hawaii. It is a semi-evergreen shrub (6-15 ft. tall) with arching branches and leaves (to 1 in. long) silvery-velvet beneath. Loaded with showy fruits in winter. Grown from seeds, cuttings or layers.

CHINESE HAWTHORN (*Photinia serrulata*), a favorite ornamental in its native China, California and other mild climates, is a shrub or small tree (to 30-40 ft.). Its leaves are coppery-red when young, crimson before falling. Flowers (in 6 in. clusters) in summer; fruits vivid fall-winter. Needs part shade.

NARROW-LEAVED FIRETHORN (*Pyracantha angustifolia*), a shrub (to 10-12 ft.) of southwest China, is the species best suited to mild climates. Its long, drooping, thorny branches are downy when young. Leaves (¾-2¼ in. long) are velvety gray beneath, and the young fruits gray and fuzzy. Smooth, ripe fruits make a striking show.

INDIAN HAWTHORN (*Raphiolepis indica*), of southern China, is a shrub (to 5 ft.) with slim, spreading branches, leathery leaves (1½ to 2½ in. long) and white or pink flowers. Very slow-growing. Stands full sun, poor soil, and salt spray.

YEDDO HAWTHORN (*Raphiolepis umbellata*), from southern Japan, is an upright shrub (to 12 ft.) with thick leaves (1½ to 3 in. long) and fragrant flowers. Of moderate growth rate; very wind- and salt-resistant. Fruits are pear-shaped and blue-black.

PEA FAMILY (Leguminosae) is the third largest among flowering plants, with 600 genera and 12,000 species in three groups: Lotoideae, or Papilionateae (mainly temperate, with flowers always "pealike"), Caesalpinoideae, and Mimosoideae (both mainly tropical). Plant types include annual and perennial herbs, shrubs, vines and trees; some aquatic, some xerophytic. All bear seedpods with or without pulp. Many genera are of great importance economically, furnishing food, fodder, timber, gum, oil and dye. Some are notorious for their toxic properties; many are outstanding ornamentals.

FLAME AMHERSTIA (*Amherstia nobilis*), from Burma, is a renowned tree (30-40 ft.) with pinnate leaves, the leaflets 6 to 12 in. long. Flower sprays reach 2 to 3 ft. Rare and difficult to raise. Grown from seeds (few produced), cuttings or layers.

WOMAN'S TONGUE *(Albizia lebbeck)*, from tropical Asia and northern Australia, is a broad-topped tree (to 100 ft. tall) with pinnate leaves (to 15 in. long), shed in winter when the abundant dry pods rattle in the wind. Grows rapidly from seed.

SILK TREE *(Albizia julibrissin)*, native to mild areas from Iran to Japan, is a broad tree (to 40 ft.) with deciduous, feathery leaves (9-10 in. long), blooming heavily in summer. Popular in California; and is the common "mimosa" of the South.

BAILEY ACACIA *(Acacia baileyana)*, of New South Wales, is highly prized there and in California. A shrub or tree (10 to 30 ft.) with bluish foliage, it has a rich show of flowers in late winter. Variety *purpurea* has purple-tinted foliage.

PURPLE ORCHID TREE (*Bauhinia purpurea*), from India and China, is a full-headed tree (to 40 ft.). In fall, it bears orchidlike, purple, red or lavender flowers (to 5 in. wide) amidst the foliage (p. 51). Later, there is a heavy crop of flat seedpods which snap open, scattering their brown seeds. A very similar, lavender-flowered tree (*B. variegata*) and its white-flowered variety *candida* bloom in spring after their leaves have fallen. These are fast-growing trees, raised from seeds which remain viable more than a year.

FLAME-OF-THE-FOREST (*Butea frondosa*), a native of India, is a homely tree (20-50 ft. high) with crooked trunk and branches. The trifoliate leaves with gray-green leaflets (4-8 in. long) are shed in midwinter. Soon after, the ends of the branches are covered for 2 or 3 ft. with black, velvety buds from which emerge the lovely flowers, making a breathtaking display. The tree is featured in Hindu ceremonies and folklore. Grown from seeds or cuttings in Florida. Does well in salty soils.

ST. THOMAS TREE (*Bauhinia tomentosa*), native to tropical Africa, China and India, is a small tree or shrub (to 15 ft.) with thin leaves (1½ to 3 in. wide) and drooping flowers that do not fully open. Seeds are difficult to germinate.

RED BAUHINIA (*Bauhinia galpini*), from tropical Africa, is a drought-resistant, sprawling or climbing shrub with evergreen leaves (2-3 in. wide), blooming profusely all summer. Would be more common, but seedpods are scarce and cuttings hard to root.

MOUNTAIN ROSE (*Brownea grandiceps*), native to northern Venezuela, is an evergreen tree (to 40 or 60 ft.) with pinnate leaves (to 15 in. long), drooping decoratively when young. The flowers are massed in spectacular, rose-like heads (to 8 in. wide) in terminal spikes. Introduced into Europe in 1803 and much admired in tropical botanic gardens, the tree is successful in Hawaii but uncommon in Florida and California. Grown from cuttings and seeds scarified before planting. Slow-growing.

Flame-of-the-Forest

Purple
Orchid Tree

St. Thomas Tree

Red Bauhinia

Mountain Rose

51

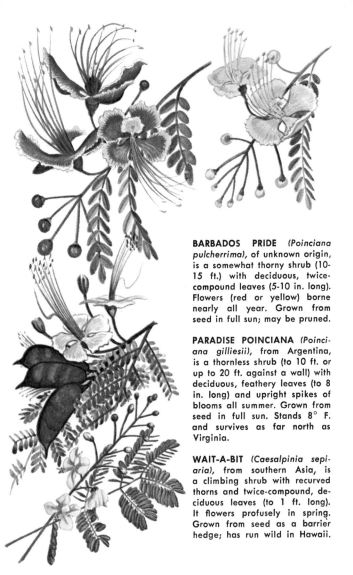

BARBADOS PRIDE (*Poinciana pulcherrima*), of unknown origin, is a somewhat thorny shrub (10-15 ft.) with deciduous, twice-compound leaves (5-10 in. long). Flowers (red or yellow) borne nearly all year. Grown from seed in full sun; may be pruned.

PARADISE POINCIANA (*Poinciana gilliesii*), from Argentina, is a thornless shrub (to 10 ft. or up to 20 ft. against a wall) with deciduous, feathery leaves (to 8 in. long) and upright spikes of blooms all summer. Grown from seed in full sun. Stands 8° F. and survives as far north as Virginia.

WAIT-A-BIT (*Caesalpinia sepiaria*), from southern Asia, is a climbing shrub with recurved thorns and twice-compound, deciduous leaves (to 1 ft. long). It flowers profusely in spring. Grown from seed as a barrier hedge; has run wild in Hawaii.

RED POWDERPUFF (*Calliandra haematocephala*) is a large tropical American shrub (12-25 ft.), wide-spreading, with evergreen, twice-pinnate foliage. Blooms in winter. Grown from air-layers or cuttings in sun. May be pruned to desired size.

EAST AFRICAN LABURNUM (*Calpurnia subdecandra*) is a shrub or small tree (10-20 ft.) with evergreen leaves (4-10 in.) and laburnum-like flowers in winter. The pods persist a long time. Grown as an ornamental and as a shade for coffee trees.

CANDLEBUSH (*Cassia alata*), a tropical American shrub (to 15 ft.), often sprawling, has compound leaves (to 3 ft. long) and brilliant blooms in fall and winter. Grown from seeds in full sun and cut back in spring. Widely known as "ringworm bush," the leaves are a common folk remedy for skin afflictions.

GOLDEN SHOWER (*Cassia fistula*), from India, is a fast-growing tree (25-60 ft.) with compound leaves (to 20 in. long), mostly shed as the tree becomes draped with blooms (June to August). The fruits are the Cassia pods well known in the drug trade for their laxative pulp.

PINK-AND-WHITE SHOWER (*Cassia javanica*), native to the East Indies, is a tree (15-45 ft.) with thornlike spurs. The compound leaves (6-12 in. long) fall in winter and new foliage appears in early summer with the flowers, much like apple blossoms. Grows rapidly from seed in full sun.

MORETON BAY CHESTNUT *(Castanospermum australe),* from New South Wales, is a majestic, low-branching tree (40-90 ft., or up to 130 ft. in the wild). The evergreen, compound leaves (1-1½ ft. long) partly hide the flowers that are massed along the older limbs and often on the trunk in midsummer and succeeded by glossy, decorative pods. The tree is planted for shade in California and on the Riviera. Grows fast in moist, rich soil; needs full sun. The leaves and pods are toxic to livestock, but the seeds, after long soaking and roasting, are ground into an edible meal.

GLORY PEA *(Clianthus dampieri),* from Australia, is a bushy perennial, semi-erect (2-4 ft.) or reclining. The stems and compound leaves (5-7 in.) are coated with grayish, silky hairs. Grown from scarified seed but longer-lived if grafted onto *Colutea arborescens.* Prized for rock gardens and hanging baskets.

BUTTERFLY PEA *(Clitoria ternatea),* found wild throughout India, is a slender, twining vine (to 20 ft.) with compound leaves (4-6 in. long). Flowers (typically blue, may be pink or white; sometimes double) appear in summer or nearly all year. Cut blooms keep well. Vine fast-growing in full sun, moist soil.

COLVILLE'S GLORY (*Colvillea racemosa*), of Madagascar, is an erect, moderately spreading tree (40-50 ft.) with tall trunk and flaking bark. The feathery leaves (to 3 ft. long) are shed in winter right after the blooming season, which lasts about 6 weeks. Flower spikes (to 8 in. long), in drooping or erect clusters (1½-2 ft. long), stand out above the foliage. Slow-growing from seed, borne in cylindrical, 6-in. pod, which is not produced in Florida. Seedlings may bloom in 2 years or not for 10. Widely distributed but not commonly seen in any area.

SAPUPIRA (*Bowdichia virgilioides*), native to Guyana and adjacent areas of Brazil and Venezuela, ranges from a small tree (10-15 ft.) to a forest giant (up to 150 ft.). Its compound leaves are shed in winter before the flowers appear in large, terminal sprays. Thin, wine-red pods used in perfumery.

LANCEPOD (*Lonchocarpus sericeus*), native to tropical West Africa and naturalized in tropical America and West Indies, is a shrub or tree (to 50 or even 100 ft.), with brownish, downy branchlets and pinnate foliage. The flowers appear after the leaves are shed in the dry season. Seeds, in woody pod, toxic.

JEWEL VINE *(Derris scandens)*, native from India to Australia, is a woody vine (to 15-35 ft.) with evergreen, compound leaves and flower clusters (to 1 ft. long) in summer and fall. Grown from seed or cuttings in moist soil; sun or partial shade.

ROYAL POINCIANA *(Delonix regia)*, from Madagascar, is an umbrella-topped, low-branching tree (to 60 ft.) with feathery leaves (to 2 ft. long). Famed for its vivid (red or yellow) blooms in summer; mostly bare in winter except for pods (to 2 ft.). Fast-growing from seed.

JADE VINE (Strongylodon macrobotrys), a Philippine vine, high-twining, has trifoliolate leaves and drooping flower clusters (to 3 ft. long) all spring and summer. Slow-growing from seeds or air-layers; blooms in 3 years. Flowers used in leis.

INDIAN CORAL TREE (Erythrina variegata var. orientalis), native from India to Polynesia, is a thorny tree (to 60 ft.) with trifoliate leaves, shed in late winter, just before the flowers appear. Cuttings 6 ft. long take root readily.

MOUNTAIN IMMORTELLE (Erythrina poeppigiana), native from Panama to Bolivia, is a spiny tree (to 80 ft.) which may have some leaves when it flares into bloom in spring. Cuttings grow fast. Often planted as shade for cacao and coffee trees.

MADRE DE CACAO (*Gliricidia sepium*), of tropical America and the West Indies, is a small tree (to 30 ft.) with spreading branches which shed their pinnate leaves in late winter and are soon densely covered with bloom. Commonly planted in the tropics as shade for cacao, support for vanilla and black pepper vines, and for living-fence-posts, since limbs thrust into the ground take root and grow rapidly in dry soil. Also grown from seed (in 5- to 6-in. pods). The flowers are cooked and eaten. Leaves, seeds, and bark long reputed to be rat poisons but have not proved so in trials.

PURPLE SARSAPARILLA (*Hardenbergia violacea*), from Australia and Tasmania, a climbing shrub, has smooth, twining stems, stiff, evergreen leaves (1½-5 in. long) and quantities of flowers in spring. There are white- and pink-flowered varieties. Grown from cuttings.

59

JERUSALEM THORN (*Parkinsonia aculeata*), despite its common name, is a tropical American tree (to 30 ft.), naturalized from Florida to California and widely planted in the Old World. It is green-trunked when young and has a light, airy appearance with its slim, green branches and curious leaves disguised as flat, slender "needles" (8-16 in. long) bearing sharp spines and tiny leaflets (1/16-5/16 in.). The fragrant flowers appear throughout spring and summer. Seeds are produced in lumpy pods (2-6 in. long). Fast-growing from seeds, cuttings or air-layers. Needs full sun; tolerates drought, also low, moist, salty soil and indirect exposure to salt spray, but is lusher in good soil and inland location. Popular in Florida landscaping.

COPPERPOD (*Peltophorum pterocarpum*), from Malaysia, is a broad-topped tree (to 60 or even 100 ft.) with compound leaves (1 to 2 ft. long), evergreen except in dry locations. There is a conspicuous reddish-brown fuzz on the stalks and buds of the flower clusters. The brilliant sprays of flowers which stand out above the foliage (spring to fall) emit a grapelike perfume at night. They are succeeded by flat, maroon seedpods which are attractive until they blacken. Fast-growing from seeds. Long known as *P. inerme*. Often called "yellow poinciana" but this name should be limited to the yellow variety of Royal Poinciana (*Delonix regia*)—see on p. *57*.

ASOKA TREE (*Saraca indica*), from India and Malaya, is a tree (to 30 ft.) sacred to the Hindus. Leaves are evergreen, compound, to 1 ft. long. The flowers (in spring) are orange when first open; later red. They are fragrant and used in decorating temples and worn in the hair. Seedpods (to 10 in. long) red when unripe; black when ripe. Easily grown from seeds.

TREE FUCHSIA (*Schotia brachypetala*), from South Africa, is a tree (to 40 ft.) with compound leaves which are shed in late winter. Flowers borne in terminal clusters or on older branches and trunk (in spring). Brown, woody seedpods (to 4 in. long) remain on the tree a long time. Slow-growing from seed, in dry soil; tolerates drought.

MESCAL BEAN (*Sophora secundiflora*), native from New Mexico and Texas into Mexico, is a shrub or tree (to 35 ft.) with evergreen, compound leaves (4-6 in. long). The violet-scented flowers in terminal clusters (spring and summer) are followed by silvery pods that split open, revealing the attractive seeds. These contain the alkaloid, cytisine, and as little as one seed has caused fatal poisoning in humans. Nevertheless, southwestern Indians have used the powdered seeds to produce inebriation and deep slumber. Slow-growing from seeds; needs full sun and ample watering. Sometimes espaliered on a wall. A popular ornamental in India. Highly prized in California.

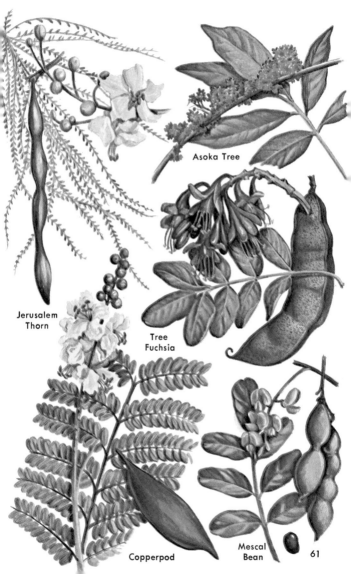

Asoka Tree

Jerusalem
Thorn

Tree
Fuchsia

Copperpod

Mescal
Bean

61

GANSIES *(Sutherlandia frutescens)*, from South Africa, is a downy shrub (5-15 ft. high) with evergreen, compound leaves (2½-3½ in. long). The flowers appear in drooping sprays in spring. Seedpods (to 2 in. long), papery and inflated, are also showy. Fast-growing from seeds or cuttings in full sun.

DARLING PEA *(Swainsonia galegifolia)*, from Queensland and New South Wales, is a subshrub, spreading (1-3 ft. high) or climbing if given support. It has feathery foliage and blooms continuously. Flowers may be scarlet, bronze, mauve, pink, or white. Grown from seeds or cuttings. Pruned in winter.

TIPA *(Tipuana tipu)*, from Bolivia and Argentina, is a tree (30-100 ft.), common along roads in South America, Algeria and the Riviera. It has deciduous, compound leaves (8-10 in. long), and flowers in loose terminal clusters in summer. Winged seeds persist nearly all year. Grows fast in dry soil.

CARIB WOOD (*Sabinea carinalis*), of Dominica, is a small tree often cultivated for ornament in the West Indies. Its fine, feathery foliage is shed in winter, and the vivid flowers emerge before the new leaves, in spring. Grown from seed (in 4-in. pods) or cuttings, in full sun, preferably on dry soil.

GUAPIRUVU (*Schizolobium parahyba*), native from Brazil to Mexico, is a slender tree (50-120 ft.), often buttressed, with fern-like leaves (to 4 ft. long). The bare branches put forth an abundance of blooms in erect clusters (to 1 ft. tall) in winter. Fast-growing from seed (borne in pods to 4 in. long).

63

CALTROP FAMILY (Zygophyllaceae)

VERA (*Bulnesia arborea*), native to northern Venezuela and Colombia, is a tree (35-120 ft.) with a tall, straight trunk and evergreen, compound leaves. Flowers are borne in short clusters in summer and fall. Occurs in arid regions. Slow-growing. Wood is heavy and hard and has been used for brush backs and as bearings for machinery. Vera posts in 300-year-old ruins were found to be in good condition.

LIGNUM VITAE (*Guaiacum officinale*), native to the West Indies, northern South America and Panama, is a tree (15-30 ft.) with compound, evergreen leaves (1½-3 in. long), blooming and bearing clusters of fruits continuously from spring to fall. The self-lubricating, heavy, hard wood, formerly used for bowling balls, is unequalled for lining propeller shafts of ships. Very slow-growing from seed.

PUNCTURE VINE (*Tribulus cistoides*), found in Florida and on most tropical coasts, is a prostrate herb with hairy stems reaching 20 in. and pinnate leaves (1½-3 in. long). Everblooming flowers open in morning and close at noon. Forms great carpets of color in the wild and is often planted as a ground cover where its spiny fruits will not be troublesome. Best grown from cuttings; grows well on dry, sandy soil and fully exposed to salt spray.

RUE FAMILY (Rutaceae)

BREATH-OF-HEAVEN *(Diosma ericoides)*, from South Africa, is a bushy shrub (to 3-4 ft.) with alternate, evergreen, aromatic leaves (1/8 to 1/4 in. long). The flowers, white or reddish, are borne all spring and summer. Popular in greenhouses and often planted as a hedge in California. Stands light clipping. Branches used in florists' arrangements. Grown from cuttings, in poor soil.

ORANGE JASMINE *(Murraya paniculata)*, from southern Asia and the East Indies, is a graceful shrub or short-trunked, round-topped tree (to 25 ft.) with attractive, evergreen, compound leaves and very fragrant flowers followed by bright red fruits. Easily grown from seed, but cuttings difficult to root. Popular as a clipped hedge. Wood has been used for canes; roots for dagger handles.

MAYPOLE *(Spathelia simplex)*, a native of Jamaica, is a curious tree (20-25 ft.) with a single slender trunk only 3 in. wide at the ground, unbranched but roughened by old leaf scars. The compound, fernlike leaves (16 in.-5 ft. long) are clustered at the summit and are velvety on the underside. Flowers are borne in a terminal spray (to 6 ft. high and 8 ft. broad). Six months after producing seeds (in 3-sided, 3-winged fruits), the tree dies.

SIMARUBA FAMILY (Simarubaceae)

BITTERWOOD (*Quassia amara*) is a shrub or small tree (rarely 25 ft.) from northern Brazil to Mexico and West Indies. Mature leaves (to 4 in. long) are dark green and glossy above, light beneath; new leaves are scarlet. Flowers (never open fully) and small fruits hang in loose clusters. The wood, formerly a source of tonic, is now used for insecticide. Grown from seeds or cuttings for showy flowers in the tropics, in southern California, and in greenhouses.

MAHOGANY FAMILY (Meliaceae)

CHINABERRY (*Melia azedarach*) is a tree (to 40 ft.) from western Asia, widely grown for shade in warm areas. The leaves are twice compound, 1-3 ft. long, with many leaflets, and are shed in winter. Clusters of small, lilac-scented flowers appear in spring. The abundant (but toxic) fruits are striking when tree is bare. It is short-lived, fast-growing, from seeds which are sometimes strung as beads or rosaries. Texas Umbrella tree is a broad-topped variety.

CAPE MAHOGANY (*Trichilia emetica*) is a handsome tree to 40 or 70 ft. or more, commonly found wild and planted along streets from Arabia to South Africa. The compound leaves are up to 18 in. long. Although the flowers are more fragrant than showy, the ripe, split fruits are striking—their brown or black seeds, partly encased by the orange arils, resembling doll's eyes. Oil from the seeds is important in soap making. The red wood is used in carpentry.

MALPIGHIA FAMILY (Malpighiaceae)

SHOWER-OF-GOLD (*Galphimia glauca*), from Central America and Mexico and widely cultivated, is a graceful shrub (3 to 10 ft.) with very slender, reddish branches and leaves to 3 in. long. Flowers (in spikes 3-4 or up to 8 in. tall) are often sold in bunches in Guatemalan markets. Blooms nearly all year in tropics but not in winter in Florida and southern California. Propagated by ripe wood cuttings or seeds. Needs dry soil, full sun and occasional pruning.

SARABATUCU (*Heteropteris chrysophylla*), a twining vine from Brazil, is one of the showiest members of its genus. It has reddish-brown fuzz on its branches and calyces, and its leaves (to 5 in.) are velvety golden-brown beneath. The flowers change from orange to reddish and then give way to the attractive masses of winged seeds. Propagated by cuttings.

AMAZON VINE (*Stigmaphyllon ciliatum*) is a woody evergreen vine from Brazil, with hairlike teeth on margins of the 2-3 in. leaves. It blooms from late spring to fall. The similar, denser *S. littorale*, bears smaller, deep-gold flowers in larger clusters for a shorter season. Young leaves of both are reddish. Fast-growing from cuttings; needs partial shade.

MILKWORT FAMILY (Polygalaceae)

VIOLET TREE *(Securidaca longipedunculata)* is a shrub or small tree (to 20-30 ft.), widespread across tropical Africa and south to the Transvaal. Its leaves are deciduous (½-2¼ in. long). The profusion of violet-scented flowers, from August to November, has inspired many efforts at cultivation, but this coveted species continues to be a horticultural challenge.

DALMAIS MILKWORT *(Polygala dalmaisiana)*, a hybrid that originated in France in 1839, is a 2- to 6-foot shrub which may have both alternate and opposite leaves (1 in. long). Its foliage is scant but it blooms most of the year. Popular in greenhouses and in southern California and other mild areas. Grown from layers; stands drought and light frost.

EASTERFLOWER *(Securidaca diversifolia)*, native and common in forests from northern South America to Mexico and in some of the Lesser Antilles, is a slender woody vine, trailing or high-climbing. The leaves (1-5 in. long), nearly round or pointed-oval, are hairy beneath. Often mistaken for a legume because of its pealike flowers, rose or purple, borne in terminal sprays throughout February or later. Grown from seed (winged, 1¾-2¾ in. long). Needs partial shade and constant moisture.

SPURGE FAMILY (Euphorbiaceae), one of the largest and most important plant families of warm areas, includes some 250 genera and over 4,000 species. Spurges range from herbaceous weeds to fleshy, cactuslike shrubs (many with thorns) and large, woody trees. Most have sticky, milky sap (latex), generally irritating to the skin. Typical fruits contain 3 seeds, more or less toxic. Flowers, usually small and inconspicuous, may be encircled by colorful bracts (modified leaves), as in Poinsettia (p. 70). Other ornamentals are prized for their foliage (below and p. 71). The cactuslike euphorbias (p. 70) thrive in arid regions.

CROTON (*Codiaeum variegatum*), a shrub to 15 ft., native from Fiji to Australia, is green-leaved in the wild form. Leaves (3 to 10 in.) of cultivated crotons are splashed or striped with colors; vary in shape from broad to narrow; may be lobed, wavy or spirally twisted. Cultivation, as specimens or in hedges, began in the Moluccas and has spread to all tropical and subtropical areas and northern conservatories. There are hundreds of named varieties. Small flowers are borne in terminal spikes. The common name, unfortunately, causes confusion with the dangerous Purging Croton (*Croton tiglium*). Propagation is by air-layering or 12-18 in. cuttings which root easily. Often grown in full sun; lusher and more colorful in semi-shade.

SCARLET PLUME (*Euphorbia fulgens*) is a popular shrub of southern Mexico and northern greenhouses, reaching 4 ft. and having slim, wiry, arching stems set with 2- to 4-in. leaves and tiny flowers encircled by showy bracts. Sprays are sold by florists in winter.

CROWN-OF-THORNS (*Euphorbia milii*) is a sprawling or climbing plant (1-4 ft.) from Madagascar. Its cylindrical stems are thickly clothed with spines but sparsely foliaged. Minute flowers are flanked by saucerlike bracts, which may be red, salmon-pink, or yellow-and-red.

POINSETTIA (*Euphorbia pulcherrima*), from Mexico and Central America, is a shrub (to 15 ft.) beloved as a symbol of Christmas. Its whorls of upper leaves, red, pink, salmon, pale-yellow or white, masquerading as blooms (10 to 22 in. wide), are actually splendid ruffs encircling the true, yellow-and-green flowers. Single, double and pinwheel forms grow from cuttings.

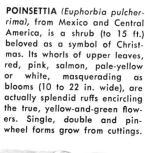

JACOB'S COAT (*Breynia nivosa*), from the Pacific Islands, is a slender, erect shrub (to 8 ft. high, 4 ft. wide) with wiry, somewhat zigzag branches and dainty leaves (1-2 in.), mottled green-and-white. Most popular variety is *roseo-picta* (shown), its leaves having added hues of red and pink. Flowers are tiny and greenish. Creeping roots send up new shoots which form clumps. Grown by root-cuttings.

CHENILLE PLANT (*Acalypha hispida*), possibly from New Guinea, East Indies or Burma, is a shrub (to 15 ft.) with leaves to 8 in. long. It is widely grown for its drooping spikes of female flowers, usually dark red, which have inspired the nickname "red-hot cattail". Variety *alba* has ivory-white spikes. In variety *ramosa*, spikes are branched. Apparently, only pistillate plants are in cultivation. Raised from cuttings in sun or light shade; moist soil.

COPPERLEAF (*Acalypha wilkesiana*), a shrub (10-15 ft.) from the South Sea Islands, is grown in most warm areas, often as a hedge. Leaves (to 10 in.) are variously mottled and blotched with brown, pink, red, bronze, orange or yellow, and sometimes edged with white. The Bahamian name, Match-me-if-you-can, reflects the fancy that no two leaves are alike. In Fiji, some believe that chewing the leaves gives magical protection from harm. Propagated by cuttings.

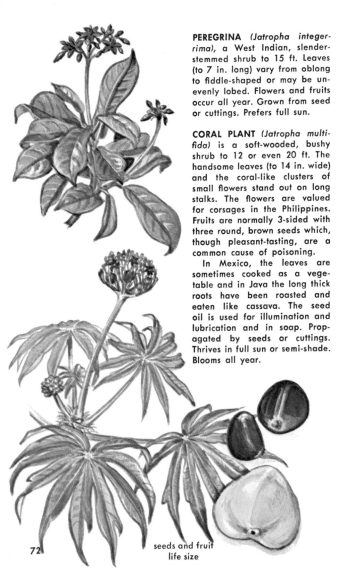

PEREGRINA (*Jatropha integerrima*), a West Indian, slender-stemmed shrub to 15 ft. Leaves (to 7 in. long) vary from oblong to fiddle-shaped or may be unevenly lobed. Flowers and fruits occur all year. Grown from seed or cuttings. Prefers full sun.

CORAL PLANT (*Jatropha multifida*) is a soft-wooded, bushy shrub to 12 or even 20 ft. The handsome leaves (to 14 in. wide) and the coral-like clusters of small flowers stand out on long stalks. The flowers are valued for corsages in the Philippines. Fruits are normally 3-sided with three round, brown seeds which, though pleasant-tasting, are a common cause of poisoning.

In Mexico, the leaves are sometimes cooked as a vegetable and in Java the long thick roots have been roasted and eaten like cassava. The seed oil is used for illumination and lubrication and in soap. Propagated by seeds or cuttings. Thrives in full sun or semi-shade. Blooms all year.

seeds and fruit
life size

GOUT PLANT (*Jatropha podagrica*), from Central America and sometimes called Guatemala rhubarb, is a single-stemmed shrub (to 5 ft.) with a swollen base. Leaves are 4 to 10 in. wide. Male flowers are scarlet; female, green. Grown from seeds.

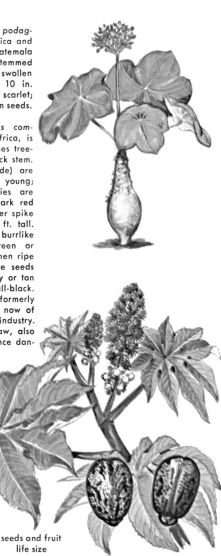

CASTOR BEAN (*Ricinus communis*), from tropical Africa, is a giant herb that becomes tree-like (to 40 ft.) with a thick stem. Leaves (1 to 3 ft. wide) are silky and bronze when young; leaves of some varieties are white-veined or solid dark red with red stems. The flower spike varies from 6 in. to 2 ft. tall. When immature, the burrlike fruits may be blue-green or red. They turn brown when ripe and burst, scattering the seeds (¼ to ¾ in. long), gray or tan mottled with brown, or all-black. Seeds yield castor oil, formerly much used medicinally, now of more importance in industry. They are toxic when raw, also contain an allergen, hence dangerous to use.

seeds and fruit
life size

CASHEW FAMILY
(Anacardiaceae)

PEPPER TREE *(Schinus molle)* is a broad, short-trunked Peruvian tree (to 40 or 50 ft. high) much grown in Central America, Mexico, California and on the Riviera, though it is host to black scale, a hazard to *Citrus* culture. Fruiting sprays are used for decoration, as are those of Brazilian Pepper *(S. terebinthifolius)* in Hawaii and Florida. Both trees are fast-growing and self-seeding; tend to become weeds.

SOAPBERRY FAMILY (Sapindaceae)

GOLDENRAIN TREE *(Koelreutaria formosana),* from Japan and Formosa, is a deciduous tree (to 40 or 60 ft.) with twice-compound leaves (1½-2 ft. long). In autumn, large flower clusters rise above the foliage, followed by even more showy masses of papery, balloonlike fruits. The summer-blooming *K. paniculata* is suited to cooler regions.

TULIPWOOD *(Harpullia pendula)* is a handsome Australian tree with weeping branches and evergreen, compound leaves. The drooping terminal clusters of small flowers develop into very showy bunches of fruits (1-1½ in. wide), hollow except for a shiny black seed in each lobe. The Asiatic *H. arborea* is similar. Both are rapid growers.

MELIANTHUS FAMILY
(Melianthaceae)

NATAL BOTTLEBRUSH *(Greyia sutherlandii)* is a South African shrub or small tree (to 15 ft. high and 12 ft. wide). In winter or spring it sheds many leaves and blooms profusely for several weeks. The flowers are 1½ in. long in 8-10 in. spikes. Grown from seed or softwood cuttings. Stands fairly poor soil, full sun, and light frosts. Popular in greenhouses and outdoors in subtropical climates.

BUCKTHORN FAMILY (Rhamnaceae)

CALIFORNIA LILAC *(Ceanothus).* This is a large genus of shrubs or small trees, mostly native on the Pacific Coast of North America. Only a few species are grown as ornamentals in warm areas. *C. cyaneus* (6-8 ft.) has dark, glossy leaves. The flowers (May-June) are deep-blue, lavender, rose or white, in lilaclike clusters. *C. azureus* of Mexico (10-15 ft.) has leaves downy-white below and dark blue flowers in branching clusters. *C. arboreus* (to 20 ft.), sometimes called Island Myrtle, has gray-green leaves, velvety white below, and fragrant, pale to medium blue flowers (late winter-spring). Likes more shade and moisture than other species. There are many lovely hybrids.

LINDEN FAMILY (Tiliaceae)

STARFLOWER (*Grewia occidentalis*) is a South African shrub (5 to 10 ft. high) with soft but slightly hairy leaves (1-4 in.), flowers that may be pink or purplish, and pea-sized edible fruits. The bush is grown from seeds or hormone-treated cuttings as an informal hedge.

WHIP TREE (*Luehea speciosa*), native from Colombia to Mexico and also in Cuba, is a broad-crowned tree (80 to 100 ft. tall) often buttressed at the base. Its leaves (4-10 in.) are downy white beneath. The tree begins very young to bloom profusely. The fruit is woody and 5-angled.

HONCKENYA (*Honckenya ficifolia*) is a woody herb or shrub (6-10 ft.) abounding in damp forests of tropical Africa. It has purplish stems and rough leaves, usually 3- to 7-lobed, often entire. Flowers, purple, rarely white, are 2 to 3 in. wide, the bristly fruits up to 2½ in. long. Rope and mats are made with the jutelike stem fiber. Grown as an ornamental from seeds or root- or softwood-cuttings, below 1300 ft.

MALLOW FAMILY (Malvaceae) covers 40 or 50 genera (some say 80) and 1,000 or more species scattered across the temperate and tropical belts. They are herbs, shrubs, and soft-wooded trees with alternate, simple, often lobed, leaves. The funnelform, 5-parted flowers are typified by the fusing of the stamens into a tube or column around the pistil and vary in color from white and yellow to purple and red. The fruit is nearly always a dry seed capsule. Some members of the family are world crops such as cotton.

FLOWERING MAPLE (*Abutilon megapotamicum*) is a drooping Brazilian shrub (under 10 ft. tall) with 2- to 4-in. leaves. Flowers are borne continuously after the first 8 months. In California it is popular as a basket plant when young.

MAGA (*Montezuma speciosissima*) is a handsome evergreen tree (to 50 ft.) common wild and cultivated in Puerto Rico. It has thick, 6- to 8-in. leaves and waxy flowers nearly all year. Thrives in low, damp soil. Its hard, durable wood is prized.

CHINESE HIBISCUS *(Hibiscus rosa-sinensis)* is an Asiatic shrub (to 20 ft.) gracing all warm regions with its year-round blooms—single or double; red, orange, yellow, pink or white; to 10 in. wide; most lasting but a day, some longer. Usually grown from cuttings; may be air-layered or grafted. Shoe-blacking and mascara are made from the red flowers in China.

FRINGED HIBISCUS *(Hibiscus schizopetalus)* is a shrub from tropical East Africa, more slender and open than the Chinese species. It has arching branches and rarely reaches as high as 12 ft. The leaves vary from 2 to 6 in. long. Usually grown from cuttings although it reproduces true from seed. In Hawaii, its pollen is much used for hybridizing with the Chinese hibiscus.

Chinese Hibiscus

MAHOE (*Hibiscus tiliaceus*), at home on all tropical shores, forms low thickets in wet soil but becomes a handsome round-topped tree to 50 ft. on higher ground. Ever-blooming, 4-in. flowers are yellow when they first open in the morning and maroon before they fall at the end of the day. The buoyant wood is used as cork; the bark was long-famed for its fiber.

ILIMA (*Sida fallax*), on all the Hawaiian islands up to 2000 ft., occurs in numerous forms— some creeping, some erect shrubs to 4 ft. high. Leaves are downy, of varying form. Flowers (1 in.) range from yellow to orange or dark red. Fresh blossoms from both wild and cultivated plants were much used for leis, but paper imitations are becoming common.

s

TURK'S CAP (*Malvaviscus arboreus*), a bushy Mexican shrub (8 to 12 ft.) with leaves 3 to 5 in. long, is often called "sleeping hibiscus" because its flowers (red, white or pink) open only slightly. Propagated by cuttings for tall hedges.

OTAGO RIBBONWOOD (*Hoheria sexstylosa*) is a subtropical tree (to 25 ft.) from New Zealand with 2- to 4-in. leaves of variable form and an abundance of sweet-scented flowers. Very fast-growing and self-seeding. The wood is used for paper pulp.

◄ **PAVONIA** (*Pavonia multiflora*) is a robust Brazilian shrub with leaves 6 to 10 in. long. The oblong purple corolla of the flower and the purple calyx, which are rolled together, are cupped by numerous showy, hairy, slender red bracts.

BOMBAX FAMILY (Bombacaceae)

RED SILK COTTON (*Bombax malabaricum*) is a giant tree from India and Burma, reaching 30 ft. in less than 5 years and eventually 125 ft., with trunk over 40 ft. around and heavily buttressed. Leaves, 5- to 7-lobed, and 6-12 in. long, fall in late winter, when the great branches glow with masses of fleshy, red or orange flowers. The woody fruit contains silky floss and many tiny black seeds. The floss, much like kapok, is used in saddles and pillows. Large cuttings root readily; put forth flowers in one year.

SHAVINGBRUSH TREE (*Bombax ellipticum*) is a tropical American tree (to 30 ft.) with smooth, green bark. The leaves (usually with 5 leaflets to 12 in. long) are shed in winter; the flowers, with red, pink, or white stamens, open in spring.

FLOSS SILK TREE (*Chorisia speciosa*) is a tree (50 to 100 ft.) from Brazil and northern Argentina, very spiny when young. The leaves (to 10 in. wide) have 5 to 7 leaflets. The flowers are spectacular in late fall when the foliage is scanty.

CHOCOLATE FAMILY (Sterculiaceae)

FLAME TREE (*Brachychiton acerifolium*) is a pyramidal Australian tree to 60 ft. or more with variable, often maplelike leaves (to 10 in. wide), the oldest of which drop at blooming time (in Florida, spring; in California, July-August). The abundance of flowers makes a brilliant display. The thick bark yields a lacelike fiber (bast) prized for hats, baskets and other articles. The seedpods furnish dye.

BANGAR NUT (*Sterculia foetida*) is a tree to 100 ft. high in its natural range from tropical East Africa to Australia where it is planted along highways. The leaves (with 7 to 9 leaflets) may be 1 ft. wide and are shed in spring when the branches are tipped with large clusters of flowers broadcasting a musky, unpleasant odor. Woody pods are prized for decoration; the 1-in. seeds edible after roasting.

PINK BALL (*Dombeya* X *cayeuxii*), native to Madagascar, is a short-trunked tree to 30 ft. with downy leaves, 5 to 12 in. wide. In winter flowers are borne in numerous pendent balls, partly hidden by the dense foliage. Long known as *D. wallichii*.

ROSEMOUND (*Dombeya* sp.), developed in Miami, Florida, from seed supposedly from Réunion, is a shrub smaller in stature and foliage than the pink ball and showier. Mass plantings lovely in the fall.

DINNER PLATE TREE (*Pterospermum acerifolium*), common wild and cultivated in India and Burma, is a slender but wind-resistant tree to 40 ft. or more. The handsome leaves, from nearly round to spadelike and up to 15 in. long, are downy and conspicuously pale on the underside, and in Asia are used as plates and roof lining under thatch. The flowers, fragrant even after drying, appear in winter, followed by scurfy, woody pods containing many winged seeds. Raised from air-layers; sometimes in pots.

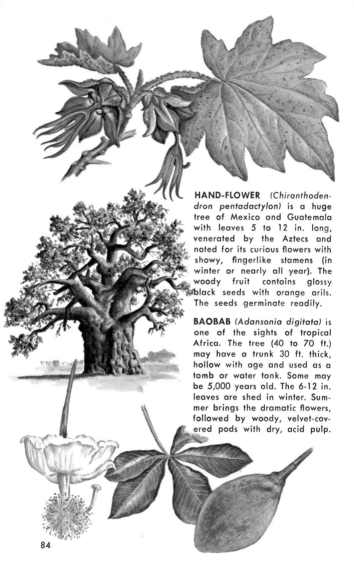

HAND-FLOWER (*Chiranthodendron pentadactylon*) is a huge tree of Mexico and Guatemala with leaves 5 to 12 in. long, venerated by the Aztecs and noted for its curious flowers with showy, fingerlike stamens (in winter or nearly all year). The woody fruit contains glossy black seeds with orange arils. The seeds germinate readily.

BAOBAB (*Adansonia digitata*) is one of the sights of tropical Africa. The tree (40 to 70 ft.) may have a trunk 30 ft. thick, hollow with age and used as a tomb or water tank. Some may be 5,000 years old. The 6-12 in. leaves are shed in winter. Summer brings the dramatic flowers, followed by woody, velvet-covered pods with dry, acid pulp.

ACTINIDIA FAMILY (Actinidiaceae)

PURPLE SIMPOH (*Wormia excelsa*), one of the most beautiful trees of Malaya (to 80 ft.) has shiny leaves (4-12 in.) and up-turned, fragrant flowers. Red fruit buds and red arils in the opened, star-shaped fruits are additional showy features.

HONDAPARA (*Dillenia indica*) is a 30- to 40-foot tree found wild from India to the Philippines. It has handsome leaves (7-12 in.), scented flowers and is popular as an ornamental. A thick, fleshy calyx envelops the muci-laginous fruit.

OCHNA FAMILY (Ochnaceae)

CHERRY RED OCHNA (*Ochna mechowiana*) is a small tree of Central Africa (to 10 ft.). The lovely flowers open early in the morning; lose their petals by noon. The fruits, like those of other ochnas, are attached to very showy calyces.

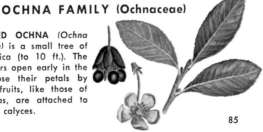

85

TEA FAMILY (Theaceae)

CAMELLIAS, from Japan, Korea and China, are evergreen shrubs or trees prized in greenhouses and gardens for the single or double flowers—red, pink or white. *Camellia japonica* (to 30-40 ft.) best for corsages (Oct.-April); *C. sasanqua* (to 20 ft.), faster growing, with smaller blooms (Sept.-Dec.). Grown from cuttings, layers, seeds, grafts.

MANGOSTEEN FAMILY (Guttiferae)

PITCH APPLE (*Clusia rosea*) is a West Indian tree (to 30-60 ft.) with spreading branches and thick, rubbery leaves (to 10 in. long), beautiful, waxy flowers, pink or white with pink streaks, and resinous, woody fruits. Popular in landscaping, usually trimmed as a shrub. Grown from seeds, cuttings or air-layers.

BIXA FAMILY (Bixaceae)

ANNATTO (*Bixa orellana*), from tropical America, is a shrubby tree (to 25-30 ft.). Blooms in fall; during winter bears bunches of bur-like pods, maroon-bristled or vivid scarlet. The small seeds are coated with orange pulp rubbed by Indians on their bodies and hair and widely used as food coloring. Grown from cuttings and seeds.

BUTTERCUP TREE FAMILY (Cochlospermaceae)

BUTTERCUP TREE (*Cochlospermum vitifolium*), of Central America, is a slender tree (to 35 ft.) with deciduous leaves (6-8 in. wide). Single or double flowers grace the bare branches from late winter through spring. Pods contain white floss. Fast growing from seeds or cuttings. Blooms when only 2-3 ft. high.

FLACOURTIA FAMILY
(Flacourtiaceae)

FRIED EGG TREE (*Oncoba spinosa*), from tropical Africa, is a shrub or bushy tree (to 40 ft.), thorny, with evergreen leaves (to 4 in. long), and fragrant flowers in summer. Grown from seeds or cuttings. The hard fruits are edible but sour and seedy. Dried, hollowed-out shells used for snuff-boxes and rattles.

TURNERA FAMILY (Turneraceae)

BUTTERFLY TREE (*Erblichia odorata*), native from Mexico to Panama, is a tree (to 50 ft.) with alternate leaves (2½-5 in. long), usually downy beneath, and handsome, fragrant flowers. Considered one of the showiest trees of Central America. The seed-pod is woody, 1½ in. long.

SAGE ROSE (*Turnera ulmifolia*), native to the West Indies and tropical America, is a slender shrub (2-4 ft.) with attractive, aromatic leaves and sunny flowers that close at noon. Blooms nearly all year. Propagated by seeds, cuttings, or division. The leaf infusion is a popular tonic.

PASSION FLOWER FAMILY
(Passifloraceae)

PASSION FLOWER vines belong to the genus *Passiflora*. Of nearly 400 species, most are South American. They are evergreen vines that climb by tendrils. Some are cultivated for their edible fruits, others for the elaborate flowers which, to the early Spanish explorers, were symbolic of the Crucifixion. Garden favorites include: Blue P.F. *P. caerulea*, with 5-lobed leaves (to 4 in. wide), part-parent of many hybrids; *P. racemosa*, with leaves (3-4½ in. wide) mostly 3-lobed, and blooms in hanging clusters; and *P. coccinea*, with 2- to 3-lobed leaves (to 5 in. wide). Fast-growing from cuttings in rich, moist soil, in full sun.

CACTUS FAMILY (Cactaceae) embraces possibly 25 genera and 1,500-2,000 species, some in North America but most from tropical America and even the high altitudes farther south. They may be terrestrial, semi-epiphytic or epiphytic; denizens of arid regions or of moist forests. Only one genus, *Pereskia*, has conventional stems and leaves; other cacti exhibit a variety of forms—barrel-like, columnar, ribbed or deeply fluted; or have fleshy, cylindrical, triangular or flattened stems, some formed of a series of joints or links. Some are treelike; others climb like vines by means of aerial roots. Most cacti store water in their tissues and have spines to protect them from grazing animals. The flowers are often large and beautiful. Cacti are slow-growing; propagated by seeds or cuttings. They are easily grafted. Very few are toxic.

ROSE CACTUS (*Pereskia grandifolia*), from Brazil, is a spiny shrub or tree (6-15 ft.) with fleshy, true leaves (unusual in a cactus) 3-6 in. long. Flowers red or white. Grown for hedges in South America and widely cultivated as an ornamental.

GOOSENECK CACTUS (*Epiphyllum oxypetalum*), native from Mexico to Brazil, is a climbing plant (to 10 ft.), epiphytic or sometimes terrestrial, with thin flat stems (4-5 in. wide). The fragrant flowers open in the evening. Needs moist, rich soil.

NIGHT-BLOOMING CEREUS *(Hylocereus undatus)*, of unknown origin, is widely grown and naturalized in tropical and subtropical areas. It is semi-epiphytic, its triangular, jointed, spine-edged stems climbing walls and trees by means of aerial roots. Numerous big, heavily perfumed flowers open for a single night, in summer. Buds cut in the evening will open indoors. The deep-pink fruit has edible flesh.

INDIAN STRAWBERRY *(Echinocereus engelmanii)*, native from Mexico to Utah, forms clumps of erect, ribbed, spiny stems (4 to 15 in. high). The flowers, just below stem tips, open in daytime. The fruit is red, oval, edible. Grown from seed in sandy soil. Needs semi-shade at first.

MEZEREUM FAMILY (Thymelaceae)

DAIS (*Dais cotinifolia*), a South African shrub or tree (to 25 ft.) has deciduous leaves (3-5 in. long) and fragrant flowers in late spring and summer. Propagated by seed or suckers; cuttings do not root freely. Fast-growing in full sun; blooms when only 4 or 5 ft. high.

WRINKLED GNIDIA (*Gnidia oppositifolia*), a native of South Africa, is a moderately branched, erect, heathlike shrub (3-12 ft. high) with smooth, evergreen leaves (½ in. long) and terminal clusters of flowers in summer. Abounds along streams and marshes.

RICEFLOWER (*Pimelea ferruginea*), a native of Western Australia, is an erect, compact shrub (2-4 ft.) with evergreen leaves (¼-½ in. long), silky on the underside. The flowers are produced abundantly in spring. Very popular in greenhouses and outdoors in California. Slow growing. Propagated by cuttings. Needs subacid soil and moisture, drastic cutting back after blooming. Var. *coarctica* is prostrate; has white flowers. This species lives longer than others.

LOOSESTRIFE FAMILY (Lythraceae)

CIGAR FLOWER (*Cuphea platy-centra*), from Mexico, is a shrubby plant (12-15 in. high) with evergreen leaves (1-3 in. long). The flowers have showy, tubular calyces but no petals. Propagated by seeds, cuttings and division; needs moist soil. In Hawaii, flowers are used in leis.

QUEEN'S CRAPE MYRTLE (*Lagerstroemia speciosa*), native from India to Australia, is a broad-topped tree (to 50-80 ft.) with deciduous leaves (5-8 in. long) and erect clusters of pink or lavender flowers. Crape Myrtle (*L. indica*) is a lovely, flowering shrub; less tropical.

POMEGRANATE FAMILY (Punicaceae)

POMEGRANATE (*Punica granatum*), from southern Asia, is a shrub or tree (to 20 ft.) with deciduous leaves (1-3½ in. long), grown for its brilliant flowers and for its fruits (red or yellow) which are both decorative and edible. Flowers of some varieties are double; some red-and-yellow, or white. Propagated by seed, cuttings, layers or grafting. Needs full sun, dry soil. May live for 200 years.

BRAZIL NUT FAMILY
(Lecythidaceae)

CANNONBALL TREE (*Couroupita guianensis*), native from northern Brazil to Trinidad, is a tree (to 80-100 ft.) with deciduous leaves (to 11 in. long) and beautiful flowers on curling stems (to 7 ft. long) festooning the trunk fantastically all the way to the ground. The fruits, borne in great numbers under favorable conditions, are unpleasantly odoriferous when ripe. (They may require 18 mos. to mature.) Grown from seed.

MEMBRILLO (*Gustavia superba*), common in wet forests of Central America, is a tree (to 45 ft.) with few upright branches bearing terminal clumps of evergreen leaves (1½-4 ft. long). The flowers cluster near branch ends. Fruits, large and edible. Grows from cuttings; needs rich soil.

TERMINALIA FAMILY
(Combretaceae)

SHOWY COMBRETUM (*Combretum grandiflorum*), a native of West Tropical Africa, is a climbing shrub (to 20 ft.) with rough leaves (4-6 in. long), downy on the underside. New growth, vivid red in mid-winter, adds to the glory of the flowers. The bunches of winged seeds, turning rosy in early spring, are also ornamental. Fast-growing from seed in rich soil, full sun. Children suck nectar from the blooms.

RANGOON CREEPER (*Quisqualis indica*), from southeast Asia and the East Indies, is a large climbing shrub (to 25 ft.) with deciduous, somewhat hairy leaves. When the blades are shed, their persistent stalks become thorns. The flowers, in drooping clusters, are white when first open, later turn pink and then deep red. Fragrant in evening. Fast-growing from cuttings, layers or root-division, in rich soil, full sun. Seeds toxic in quantity.

MYRTLE FAMILY (Myrtaceae) covers from 75 to 90 genera and 2,800 to 3,000 species, chiefly Australian and tropical American. Plant forms range from prostrate shrubs to lofty trees but are always woody. Bark of the trees may be shaggy or flaking off in patches, leaving the trunk two-toned. Leaves are evergreen, usually opposite, with aromatic oil glands and often highly fragrant when crushed. The flowers feature tufts of stamens (white, yellow, lavender or red) and many are highly attractive. The dry or fleshy fruits have a small aperture at the apex, encircled by persistent calyx-lobes. In addition to the classical myrtle (*Myrtus communis*) of the Mediterranean region, the family boasts spice and fruit trees like the clove, allspice and guava, and many splendid ornamentals such as the eucalypts, which also furnish valuable timber, gum, and essential oils.

EUCALYPTUS is a genus of 500 or more species from Australia and Malaya, mainly timber trees. Young leaves opposite; old, alternate. The name refers to the bud-cap which drops off when the flowers open. Most are non-showy in bloom; a few spectacular. The Redcap Eucalyptus (*E. erythrocorys*), 15-20 ft. tall, has crimson bud-caps and golden stamens. Flame Eucalyptus (*E. ficifolia*), attaining 45 ft., is the most ornamental, with red, white or pink flowers in clusters densely set on branch ends. Popular in California; stands salt and wind. The Marri (*E. calophylla*), ranging up to 100 ft. or more, blooms every 3 years. The flowers are white, pale-yellow, or rose.

MYRTLE HEATH (*Baeckia virgata*), from Australia and New Caledonia, is an erect shrub (to 8 or 10 ft.) with wiry branches and needle-like leaves (1/3-1 in. long). It bears loose clusters of white or pink flowers in spring and summer. Sprays are sold for decoration. Grown from cuttings in light, sandy soil.

SHOWY BOTTLEBRUSH (*Callistemon speciosus*), from western Australia, is a bushy tree (to 20 ft.) with stiff leaves (3-4 in. long). The flowers appear several times a year in dense, cylindrical spikes (the largest among the bottlebrushes). Seedlings bloom in 3-6 years; cuttings in 1 year. The tree does best in moist soil. *C. viminalis* is similar.

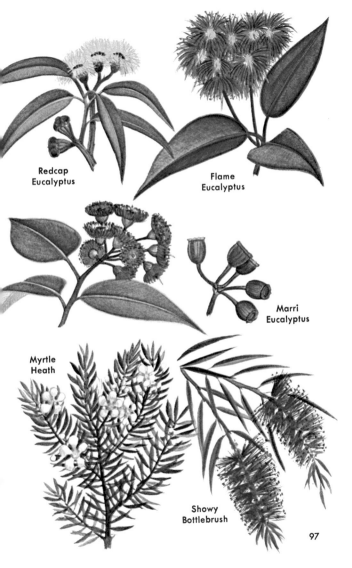

Redcap Eucalyptus

Flame Eucalyptus

Marri Eucalyptus

Myrtle Heath

Showy Bottlebrush

97

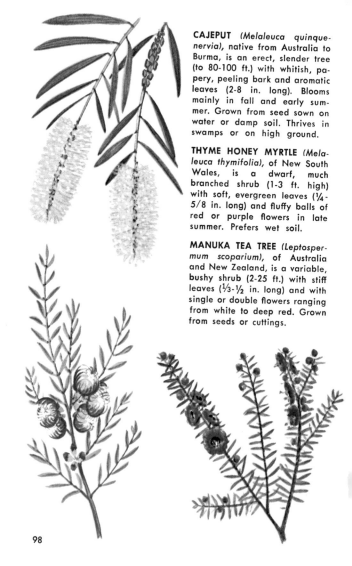

CAJEPUT (Melaleuca quinquenervia), native from Australia to Burma, is an erect, slender tree (to 80-100 ft.) with whitish, papery, peeling bark and aromatic leaves (2-8 in. long). Blooms mainly in fall and early summer. Grown from seed sown on water or damp soil. Thrives in swamps or on high ground.

THYME HONEY MYRTLE (Melaleuca thymifolia), of New South Wales, is a dwarf, much branched shrub (1-3 ft. high) with soft, evergreen leaves (¼-5/8 in. long) and fluffy balls of red or purple flowers in late summer. Prefers wet soil.

MANUKA TEA TREE (Leptospermum scoparium), of Australia and New Zealand, is a variable, bushy shrub (2-25 ft.) with stiff leaves (⅓-½ in. long) and with single or double flowers ranging from white to deep red. Grown from seeds or cuttings.

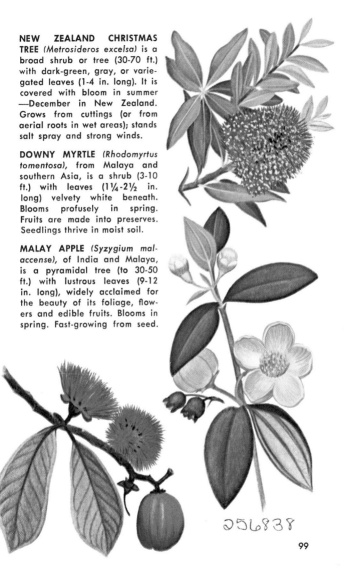

NEW ZEALAND CHRISTMAS TREE *(Metrosideros excelsa)* is a broad shrub or tree (30-70 ft.) with dark-green, gray, or variegated leaves (1-4 in. long). It is covered with bloom in summer —December in New Zealand. Grows from cuttings (or from aerial roots in wet areas); stands salt spray and strong winds.

DOWNY MYRTLE *(Rhodomyrtus tomentosa)*, from Malaya and southern Asia, is a shrub (3-10 ft.) with leaves (1¼-2½ in. long) velvety white beneath. Blooms profusely in spring. Fruits are made into preserves. Seedlings thrive in moist soil.

MALAY APPLE *(Syzygium malaccense)*, of India and Malaya, is a pyramidal tree (to 30-50 ft.) with lustrous leaves (9-12 in. long), widely acclaimed for the beauty of its foliage, flowers and edible fruits. Blooms in spring. Fast-growing from seed.

99

MELASTOMA FAMILY (Melastomaceae)

SAN MIGUEL (*Blakea gracilis*), native to Costa Rica, is a shrub or small tree (to 9-13 ft.) with slender branches and leathery, 5-nerved leaves (2½-4 in. long), glossy above and rusty-hairy on the underside. Flowers are borne singly or in pairs in late winter. Raised from cuttings in peaty, moist soil. The Jamaica Rose (*B. trinervia*) is a similar but climbing shrub with 3-nerved leaves, blooming all year.

GLORY BUSH (*Tibouchina Urvilleana*), native to Brazil, is naturalized in Hawaii and flourishes in Central Florida. It is a shrub (5-25 ft. high) with 4-sided stems and 3- to 7-nerved leaves (3-6 in. long) coated with silvery hairs. In bloom from late summer to fall or all year in some regions. Raised from cuttings or air-layers. Needs moist, acid soil. Variety *floribunda* blooms very young.

PINK GLORY BUSH (*Tibouchina sellowiana*), native to the Brazilian state of Sao Paulo, is a lovely sight along the streets and in the gardens of the city of the same name. It is a dense, low-branched shrub presenting a multitude of flowers in February, lightening in tone as they age. The purple-flowered *T. granulosa* and its pink form (variety *rosea*) bloom in April and are locally called "Flower of Lent." Need abundance of water.

OSBECKIA (*Osbeckia stellata*), native to India and China, is a shrub (to 7 ft.) with quadrangular branchlets and 5-nerved leaves (3-6 in. long) covered with stiff hairs. The flowers are borne a few together at the branch tips. This species is best-known of the 60 or more found from Africa to Australia, though several are grown in northern greenhouses. Propagated by cuttings. Needs partial shade.

MEDINILLA (*Medinilla magnifica*) is a Philippine shrub (to 3 ft.) which has been declared one of the loveliest of tropical greenhouse plants. It has 4-angled stems and evergreen, glossy leaves (to 1 ft. long). The pink or coral-red flowers, in drooping, terminal sprays, are enhanced by showy pink bracts. Grown from seeds or half-ripe cuttings. Needs moisture and light but not full sun.

EVENING PRIMROSE FAMILY (Onagraceae)

FLAME FUCHSIA (*Fuchsia fulgens*), found wild in Mexico, is a shrub (4-6 ft.) with reddish, succulent branchlets and somewhat downy leaves (3-7 in. long). Flowers dangle from leafy branch tips in summer. Grown from cuttings; needs moisture and shade. This species is a parent of some of the tender varieties. Most fuchsias are hardy plants, unsuited for cultivation in tropical and subtropical climates.

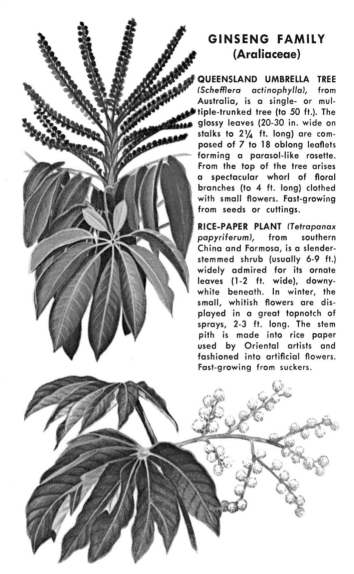

GINSENG FAMILY
(Araliaceae)

QUEENSLAND UMBRELLA TREE (*Schefflera actinophylla*), from Australia, is a single- or multiple-trunked tree (to 50 ft.). The glossy leaves (20-30 in. wide on stalks to 2¼ ft. long) are composed of 7 to 18 oblong leaflets forming a parasol-like rosette. From the top of the tree arises a spectacular whorl of floral branches (to 4 ft. long) clothed with small flowers. Fast-growing from seeds or cuttings.

RICE-PAPER PLANT (*Tetrapanax papyriferum*), from southern China and Formosa, is a slender-stemmed shrub (usually 6-9 ft.) widely admired for its ornate leaves (1-2 ft. wide), downy-white beneath. In winter, the small, whitish flowers are displayed in a great topnotch of sprays, 2-3 ft. long. The stem pith is made into rice paper used by Oriental artists and fashioned into artificial flowers. Fast-growing from suckers.

HEATH FAMILY
(Ericaceae)

BLACK-EYED HEATH (*Erica canaliculata*), from South Africa, is an erect shrub (3-5 ft.) with evergreen leaves (1/8-1/4 in. long), blooming all winter. Grown from seed or cuttings in sun or shade. Often misnamed *E. melanthera*. There are many other species cultivated in cool climates.

RHODODENDRON is a genus that embraces about 600 species of rhododendrons and azaleas, the former usually evergreen with bell-like flowers; the latter deciduous with funnelform flowers. They are propagated by cuttings or air-layers; need acid soil. *R. javanicum*, the Java Rhododendron of Malaya, is an epiphytic shrub (to 6 ft.) with leaves (to 7 in. long), scaly below. The flowers vary in color; pale to deep pinkish-coral. *R. japonicum*, the Japanese Azalea (to 8 ft.) sheds its leaves (2-4 in.) in winter. Flowers may be rose, scarlet or salmon.

MYRSINE FAMILY (Myrsinaceae)

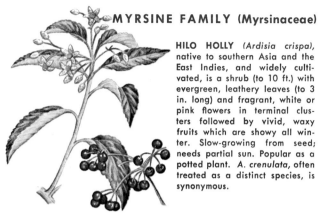

HILO HOLLY (*Ardisia crispa*), native to southern Asia and the East Indies, and widely cultivated, is a shrub (to 10 ft.) with evergreen, leathery leaves (to 3 in. long) and fragrant, white or pink flowers in terminal clusters followed by vivid, waxy fruits which are showy all winter. Slow-growing from seed; needs partial sun. Popular as a potted plant. *A. crenulata*, often treated as a distinct species, is synonymous.

LEADWORT FAMILY (Plumbaginaceae)

CAPE LEADWORT (*Plumbago capensis*) is a South African shrub with slender stems climbing to 15 ft. but usually kept low by clipping. The leaves (to 2 in. long) are white-scurfy beneath. On the calyx of the pale-blue or white flowers are sticky hairs which aid seed dispersal by adhering to coats of animals. Best propagated by suckers or root-division.

RED LEADWORT (*Plumbago indica*), a native of southern Asia, is an erect shrub (2-4 ft.) with zigzag branches and red-tinged leaves (to 8 in. long). The flowers, in terminal spikes (to 2 ft. in length) vary from purplish-red to scarlet. Var. *coccinea*, with large, vivid blooms, is the most common form. Branches which touch ground take root at nodes.

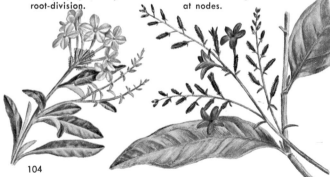

OLIVE FAMILY (Oleaceae)

ARABIAN JASMINE (*Jasminum sambac*), a native of India, is a semi-climbing shrub (to 5 ft.) with thin, evergreen leaves (1½-3 in. long). The highly fragrant flowers are white when first open; gradually turn purplish. Blooms continuously in summer and fall. Hindu people regard the flowers as sacred; the Chinese use them to flavor tea. Grown from cuttings; prefers dry soil and full sun. Grand Duke is popular double variety.

PRIMROSE JASMINE (*Jasminum mesnyi*), from western China, is a rambling shrub that can be trained as a vine (up to 15 ft.). It has arching, 4-sided branches and evergreen, trifoliate leaves, the glossy leaflets 1-3 in. long. Slightly fragrant flowers are borne singly in great abundance from winter to spring. Cut sprays keep well. Raised from cuttings or air-layers in part shade. Tolerates drought. Formerly known as *J. primulinum*.

STRYCHNINE FAMILY (Loganiaceae)

CAROLINA YELLOW JESSAMINE (*Gelsemium sempervirens*), native to the southern United States from Virginia to Texas and central Florida, is a slender, twining vine (to 20-35 ft.) with evergreen, glossy leaves (1-4 in. long). Flowers sweet-scented; midwinter-spring. Grown from cuttings in sun or semi-shade. Entire plant toxic.

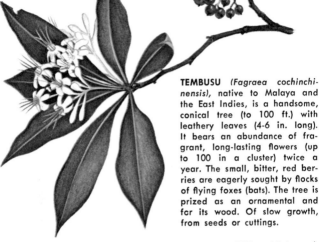

TEMBUSU (*Fagraea cochinchinensis*), native to Malaya and the East Indies, is a handsome, conical tree (to 100 ft.) with leathery leaves (4-6 in. long). It bears an abundance of fragrant, long-lasting flowers (up to 100 in a cluster) twice a year. The small, bitter, red berries are eagerly sought by flocks of flying foxes (bats). The tree is prized as an ornamental and for its wood. Of slow growth, from seeds or cuttings.

SUMMER LILAC (*Buddleia davidii*), from China, is a shrub (to 15 ft.) with deciduous leaves (4-10 in. long), velvety white beneath. Fragrant flowers appear from late summer through fall. Grown from seeds or cuttings. Var. *magnifica* is most popular.

BUTTERFLY BUSH (*Buddleia madagascariensis*), from Madagascar, a shrub (to 8-10 ft.), has slim, white, arching branches and evergreen leaves (to 6 in. long), downy-white below. Blooms January-May. Fast-growing from cuttings, in sun.

DOGBANE FAMILY (Apocynaceae) is reported to include from 180 to 300 genera and 1,000 to 1,500 species, mostly tropical, a few temperate. They are herbs, shrubs, vines (often enormous), and trees, having milky or clear, gummy sap that in some is potable, in others more or less toxic. The leaves are simple, entire, opposite or alternate and may be in whorls of three. The flowers are 5- or 4-parted; salver- or funnel-shaped. Fruits, fleshy or dry, are often borne in pairs. Members of this family are rich in alkaloids; the genus *Rauwolfia* is famed for its tranquilizing drugs; *Funtumia* is a source of rubber; *Dyera* provides a chewy substance for bubble gum, asbestos and linoleum; *Carissa* is unusual in yielding edible, popular fruits. Among the showy species are some of the most admired ornamentals of warm areas.

WINTERSWEET (*Acokanthera spectabilis*), from South Africa, is a shrub or small tree (to 15 ft.) with leathery leaves (3-5 in. long) and fragrant flowers in spring. Slow-growing. Cultivated as an ornamental but all parts, including fruits, toxic.

CONFEDERATE JASMINE (*Trachelospermum jasminoides*), from southern China, is a woody, twining vine (to 10-20 ft.) with evergreen, thick, glossy leaves (2-3 in. long). Very fragrant flowers are borne in summer. Slow-growing from cuttings.

YELLOW ALLAMANDA (*Allamanda cathartica*) is a tropical American climbing shrub (to 40 ft.) with evergreen leaves (to 6 in. long), blooming most of year. Variety *Hendersoni* has large flowers and glossy, brown buds. Grows fast from cuttings; in sun.

PURPLE ALLAMANDA (*Allamanda violacea*), from Brazil, is a slender shrub (to 10 ft.) with hairy leaves (4-6 in. long). Blooms in fall. Slow-growing, from cuttings. Stronger if grafted on Henderson *Allamanda*. Can be grown as compact vine.

HERALD'S TRUMPET (*Beaumontia grandiflora*), from India, is a heavy, woody, twining vine (to 40 ft.) with milky sap and conspicuously veined, evergreen leaves (6-12 in. long). The huge flower clusters are spectacular in spring; popular for church decoration. Propagation easiest by root-cuttings. Fast-growing with ample water and feeding. Needs full sun.

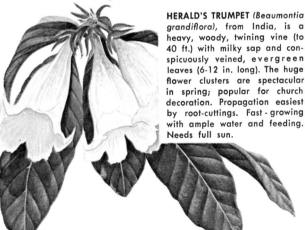

CARISSA (Carissa grandiflora), a native of South Africa, is a handsome shrub (to 15 ft.) with sharp thorns and leathery, evergreen leaves (1½-2 in. long). It bears fragrant flowers and showy fruits all year. The cut fruits exude milky sap even when ripe but are edible and agreeable raw or made into preserves. Propagated by seeds, cuttings, layers or grafting. Seedlings may not bear fruit. An ideal plant for seaside hedges; stands salt spray and wind. Dwarf forms planted as ground covers.

CRAPE JASMINE (Ervatamia divaricata), from India, is a shrub (4-8 ft.) with glossy, evergreen leaves (3-6 in. long) and milky sap. The flowers (all summer), single or double, are fragrant at night. Seedpods (1-3 in. long) in pairs, are green outside, scarlet within; split open when ripe; rarely produced in cultivation. Propagation is by layers or cuttings. Prefers full sun.

MADAGASCAR PERIWINKLE (Catharanthus roseus), native to tropical America, is a perennial herb (to 2-3 ft.) with smooth leaves (1-3 in. long), blooming all year. The flowers are white or pink, some with a dark red eye. Widely cultivated and naturalized. Long used in folk medicine, it has recently become of importance as source of drug for treating leukemia.

S

OLEANDER (*Nerium oleander*), from the Mediterranean region is an erect, many-stemmed shrub (to 20 ft.) with stiff, evergreen leaves (4-8 in. long). The fragrant, single or double, white, pink or red flowers, are continuous from spring through fall. Grown from cuttings. Though the oleander is the most popular ornamental of all warm areas, all parts are highly poisonous.

YELLOW OLEANDER (*Thevetia peruviana*), a tropical American shrub or small tree (12-20 ft.) has evergreen leaves (to 6 in. long), shining above, dull below. Blooms all year. The 4-sided fruit contains a smooth, brown stone, often called "lucky nut," strung in necklaces or carried as a charm. Grown from seeds or cuttings. May be clipped as a hedge. All parts toxic.

NOSEGAY FRANGIPANI *(Plumeria rubra)*, native from Mexico to the Guianas, is a tree (to 25 ft.) with copious milky sap, stubby branches, and handsome leaves (to 18 in.) shed in areas with dry winters. Flowers are pink, red or yellow; in variety *acutifolia*, common in India and Hawaii, white with yellow eye. After drying, large cuttings root easily, bloom soon.

WHITE FRANGIPANI *(Plumeria obtusa)*, native to the West Indies, is a many-stemmed shrub or tree (to 18 ft.) with evergreen leaves (6-8 in. long) and flowers all year. Another white-flowered West Indian species is *P. alba*, a tree (to 20 ft.), its leaves (to 15 in. long) having recurved margins and whitish down on the underside. Both flourish in very dry regions.

MILKWEED FAMILY (Asclepiadaceae) embraces about 320 genera and from 1,700 to 2,000 species, a few temperate, the majority tropical and primarily from South Africa. In the main, they are climbing shrubs or vines, but there are also perennial herbs, some succulent and leafless, resembling cacti; and most have much milky latex. Typical leaves are simple, entire, opposite. The flowers are tubular or funnel-like and 5-parted. Generally, the fruit is a dry seedpod (borne singly or in pairs), splitting and releasing seeds usually tipped with silky hairs. Some milkweeds have useful products but the best known are ornamentals.

BUTTERFLY WEED (*Asclepias curassavica*), native to tropical America, is widely naturalized and cultivated. It is an erect, perennial herb (2-5 ft. high) with smooth leaves (2-6 in. long) and conspicuous flowers (summer-fall in California; all year in Gulf States). Its seedpods contain floss used for stuffing. The plant is a host to the monarch butterfly but toxic to livestock. It is much used in tropical folk medicine. May be grown from seeds or cuttings.

WHITE BLADDER-FLOWER (*Araujia sericofera*), from southern Brazil and Peru, is a woody, twining vine (to 20-30 ft.) with downy stems and evergreen leaves (2-4 in. long) downy-white beneath. The waxy, fragrant flowers appear continuously from spring through fall. Fast-growing from seeds in part shade. Needs space. Escapes from cultivation in California. Unpleasant odor when crushed.

GIANT MILKWEED (*Calotropis procera*), native from West Tropical Africa to India, is a pale, conspicuous shrub or tree (to 18 ft.) with milky sap and thick, rubbery stems and leaves (to 12 in. long). It is everblooming, thrives on arid coasts, wholly impervious to salt spray and wind. Grown from seeds or cuttings. *C. gigantea* is similar but has pointed leaves. Both yield seedpod floss and bark fiber. All parts of the plants variously used in folk medicine.

GOLDEN HORN (*Tavaresia grandiflora*), from southwest Africa, is a leafless plant with succulent stems (to 8 in. high), having 10-14 vertical ribs bearing bristled teeth. Handsome, downward-pointing flowers (3½-5½ in. long) are borne at the base of young stems or branches in summer. Grown from seed and sometimes grafted onto the Carrion Flower. Needs full sun and dry soil; rots quickly if damp.

MADAGASCAR RUBBER VINE (*Cryptostegia madagascariensis*) is a climbing shrub from Madagascar with much milky latex and glossy, leathery leaves (2-5 in. long). Blooms all year in Florida. The very similar Palay Rubbervine (*C. grandiflora*), common in Mexico, California and dry islands of the tropics, has leaves that are hairy when young, and larger and paler flowers. Both are ornamental but toxic plants. Grow fast from seeds and cuttings.

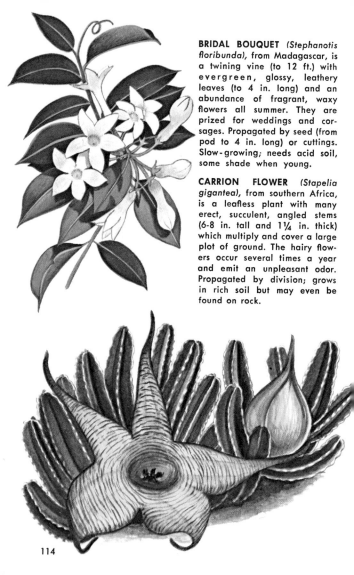

BRIDAL BOUQUET (*Stephanotis floribunda*), from Madagascar, is a twining vine (to 12 ft.) with evergreen, glossy, leathery leaves (to 4 in. long) and an abundance of fragrant, waxy flowers all summer. They are prized for weddings and corsages. Propagated by seed (from pod to 4 in. long) or cuttings. Slow-growing; needs acid soil, some shade when young.

CARRION FLOWER (*Stapelia gigantea*), from southern Africa, is a leafless plant with many erect, succulent, angled stems (6-8 in. tall and 1¼ in. thick) which multiply and cover a large plot of ground. The hairy flowers occur several times a year and emit an unpleasant odor. Propagated by division; grows in rich soil but may even be found on rock.

MORNING-GLORY FAMILY (Convolvulaceae)

CHRISTMAS VINE (*Porana paniculata*), a native of India, is a woody, twining vine (to 40 ft.), the young stems and the leaves (3-6 in. long) minutely hairy. It festoons tall trees and is a mass of flowers in early winter. Sprays are used for church decoration. Fast-growing from seeds or cuttings.

WOOLLY MORNING-GLORY (*Argyreia nervosa*), from India, is a heavy, twining vine (to 25 ft.) with downy white stems and evergreen leaves (4-12 in. long) conspicuously velvety white on the underside. Blooms in late summer. The attractive seed capsule, called "baby woodrose," is used for corsages and for earrings in Hawaii.

MOONFLOWER (*Calonyction aculeatum*), found wild in the tropics and South Florida, is a herbaceous, often prickly, vine (to 30 ft.) with silky leaves (3-8 in. long). Fragrant flowers open at night, all summer. Very fast-growing from seeds.

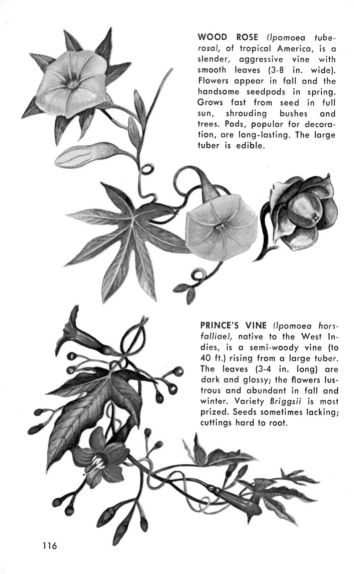

WOOD ROSE (*Ipomoea tuberosa*), of tropical America, is a slender, aggressive vine with smooth leaves (3-8 in. wide). Flowers appear in fall and the handsome seedpods in spring. Grows fast from seed in full sun, shrouding bushes and trees. Pods, popular for decoration, are long-lasting. The large tuber is edible.

PRINCE'S VINE (*Ipomoea horsfalliae*), native to the West Indies, is a semi-woody vine (to 40 ft.) rising from a large tuber. The leaves (3-4 in. long) are dark and glossy; the flowers lustrous and abundant in fall and winter. Variety *Briggsii* is most prized. Seeds sometimes lacking; cuttings hard to root.

BUSH MORNING-GLORY (*Ipomoea crassicaulis*) is found wild and cultivated from Mexico to Peru and is common in West Indian gardens. It is an erect shrub (6-8 ft.) with evergreen leaves (5-10 in. long). Delicate flowers open in morning, close in afternoon, all year. Long cuttings root quickly.

LITTLE BLUE HAT (*Jacquemontia pentantha*), of tropical America and the Florida Keys, is a slender, herbaceous, twining vine (to 10 ft.) with evergreen leaves (2 in. long). The flowers (rarely white) stand out in loose clusters in spring and summer. In variety *canescens*, the plant is coated with minute brown hairs. Grown from seeds or cuttings in partial shade.

TREE MORNING-GLORY (*Ipomoea wolcottiana*), native to southern Mexico, is a tree (to 30 ft.) with intertwining branches and deciduous leaves (3-5 in. long). Flowers open in succession for several weeks in midwinter. New foliage emerges in spring. Propagated by seeds. Cuttings reluctant to root.

117

PHLOX FAMILY (Polemoniaceae)

VIOLET IVY *(Cobaea scandens),* from Mexico, is a woody vine (to 25 ft.) with compound leaves tipped with branched tendrils (leaflets to 4 in. long). Flowers light or dark purple or white, from summer to fall. Fast-growing from seeds in moist soil, sun, or shade. Often called "cup-and-saucer vine."

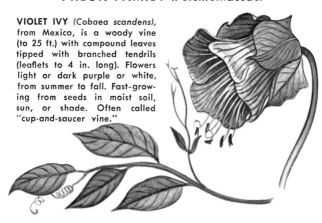

WATERLEAF FAMILY (Hydrophyllaceae)

BORRAJON *(Wigandia caras-cana),* native from Mexico to Colombia, is a hairy shrub (10-15 ft.) with handsome leaves (to 18 in. long) bearing glistening hairs that may irritate the skin. The one-sided, curving flower-spikes appear in summer. Spreading by suckers, the plant forms clumps in moist or dry soil.

HELIOTROPE FAMILY (Boraginaceae)

GEIGER TREE *(Cordia sebestena)*, native to the West Indies and Florida Keys, is a tree (to 30 ft.) with rough leaves (4-8 in. long) and orange or dark red flowers all year. Seed enclosed in fleshy, white, edible calyx. Slow-growing from seeds or cuttings. Named by Audubon for John Geiger, his host, a Key West pilot and "wrecker."

TEXAS OLIVE *(Cordia boissieri)*, from Mexico and western Texas, is a bushy shrub or tree (to 25 ft.) with rough, aromatic leaves (3-5 in. long). Flowers in spring and summer or nearly all year. Reddish-brown fruit (1-1¼ in. long), sweet and edible when cooked. Grown from seeds; blooms when very young.

ANAQUA *(Ehretia elliptica)*, native to Mexico and western Texas, is a bushy tree (to 45 ft.) with arching branches and rough leaves (1-2½ in. long). The flowers cover the tree like snow, mainly in fall or early winter, and are succeeded by an equal profusion of sweet, edible berries. Easily grown from seed.

119

VERBENA FAMILY (Verbenaceae) contains 75-100 genera and over 1,300 species of herbs, shrubs and trees, mainly subtropical or tropical in origin. Leaves, often highly aromatic, are usually opposite, sometimes whorled or alternate. Flowers are small, 4- to 5-lobed, in clusters. Fruit is a drupe, berry, or capsule. Aside from teak, few members are of outstanding economic value; the majority are ornamental.

BLUE GLORYBOWER *(Clerodendrum myricoides)*, from tropical Africa, is a compact shrub (to 8 ft.) with evergreen leaves (to 5 in. long), hairy beneath. Flowers in terminal sprays in fall, followed by black berries. Fast-growing in full sun; best on moist soil. So-called *C. ugandense* is probably a variety.

PAGODA FLOWER *(Clerodendrum paniculatum)*, native from Malaya to China, is a shrub (5-6 ft.) with long-stalked leaves (8-12 in. long). The sensational, erect flower clusters (to 18 in. tall) appear throughout summer. Grown from mature stem cuttings or root suckers. Thrives in full sun or partial shade.

enlarged 3x

BLEEDING HEART (*Clerodendrum thomsoniae*), from tropical West Africa, is a climbing, twining shrub (to 15 ft.) with evergreen leaves (to 6 in. long). Blooms in summer. Crimson flowers protrude from inflated calyces, at first white, later purplish. From seed or cuttings in moist soil, partial shade.

TUBE FLOWER (*Clerodendrum indicum*), a native of the East Indies, is a slender shrub (to 9 ft.) with erect, 4-sided stems and evergreen leaves (to 6 in. long). The flowers (late summer and fall) are succeeded by blue fruits seated on waxy, red calyces. Fast-growing from seeds in part shade; forms patches.

SHOWER-OF-ORCHIDS (*Congea tomentosa*), from southern Asia, is a massive, downy, climbing shrub with rough leaves (to 7 in. long). Tiny flowers nest in velvety bracts, in charming sprays (winter through spring). Grows from cuttings, in full sun.

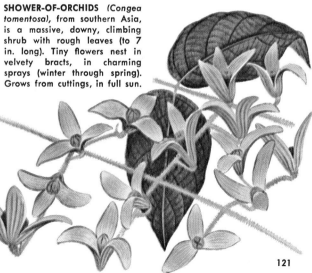

121

GOLDEN DEWDROP *(Duranta repens)*, a native of tropical America, is a bushy shrub or small tree (to 18 ft.) with slim drooping, often thorny, branches and evergreen leaves (1-4 in. long). The blue (or white) flowers (spring and summer) are followed by long-lasting, showy fruits, unwholesome for humans but eaten by birds. Grows fast from seeds or cuttings, in sun.

CHINESE HAT PLANT *(Holmskioldia sanguinea)*, from the Himalayan region, is a large sprawling or climbing shrub (to 15-30 ft.) with slender, arching branches, drooping to the ground, and evergreen leaves (1-4 in. long). The slender, tubular flower rises from a longer-lived, saucerlike calyx. Massed on branch ends; conspicuous all winter. Grown from cuttings, suckers, ground- or air-layers. Blooms in shade; becomes redder in sun.

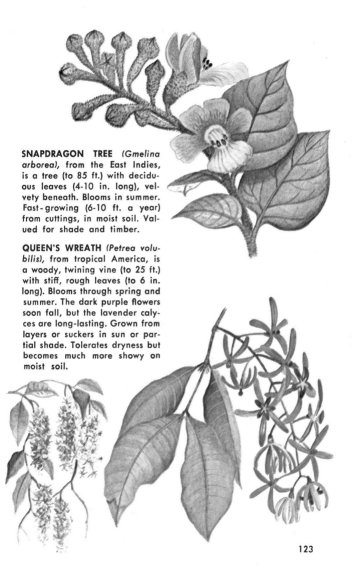

SNAPDRAGON TREE *(Gmelina arborea)*, from the East Indies, is a tree (to 85 ft.) with deciduous leaves (4-10 in. long), velvety beneath. Blooms in summer. Fast-growing (6-10 ft. a year) from cuttings, in moist soil. Valued for shade and timber.

QUEEN'S WREATH *(Petrea volubilis)*, from tropical America, is a woody, twining vine (to 25 ft.) with stiff, rough leaves (to 6 in. long). Blooms through spring and summer. The dark purple flowers soon fall, but the lavender calyces are long-lasting. Grown from layers or suckers in sun or partial shade. Tolerates dryness but becomes much more showy on moist soil.

MINT FAMILY (Labiatae) enfolds at least 160 genera and 3,000 species, most originating in temperate Asia and the Mediterranean region and high elevations of the subtropics. They are nearly all herbs (annual or perennial) or shrubs, typically with quadrangular stems. Leaves are opposite or in whorls. Flowers small, tubular, usually 5-, seldom 4-, lobed, and in erect terminal spikes or axillary clusters. Fruit 4-seeded. Many species are important flavoring and medicinal herbs and garden flowers. While a number may be grown as ornamentals in the tropics or subtropics, only a few are best suited to warm areas.

LION'S EAR (Leonotis leonurus), from South Africa, is a shrubby plant (2-7 ft. high) with downy leaves (2-5 in. long), evergreen in warm areas. The flowers (orange or, in one variety, white) continue for weeks in fall and early winter. They last well in bouquets if the stems are crushed to take up water. Grown from seed or division; in moist soil, full sun.

OVAL-LEAVED MINTBUSH (Prostanthera ovalifolia), a native of Queensland and New South Wales, is a spreading, sweetly aromatic shrub (6-8 ft. high) with fairly thick, gray-green leaves (to ½ in. long). Blooms profusely in spring. A very popular ornamental in its homeland. Readily grown from cuttings. Pruned back after flowering for compact growth.

▲
MEXICAN BUSH SAGE *(Salvia leucantha)*, from central Mexico, is a shrubby plant (to 2 ft. high), woolly-white on its young branches and underside of leaves (2-7 in. long). Flowers (in 6- to 10-in. spikes) borne in late summer. From cuttings.

DOWNY SAGE *(Salvia sessei)*, from Mexico, is a shrub (8-15 ft. high), its leaves (2-5 in. long) dotted with yellow glands on the underside. The flowers (summer-fall) are downy; the equally colorful calyces, smooth. Fast grower; pruned after blooming.

▲
IBOZA *(Iboza riparia)*, from South Africa, is a soft-wooded deciduous plant (to 12 ft. high) with aromatic leaves (1-2 in. long), blanketed with flowers in fall. Rapid-growing from cuttings. Blooming within a year. Needs post-bloom pruning.

TOMATO FAMILY (Solanaceae) embraces about 75 genera and over 2,000 species scattered over the tropical and temperate zones. The plants range from low herbs to woody vines, shrubs and small trees, many hairy or spiny. Leaves, usually alternate, may be simple or compound. Flowers, often large and handsome, are mainly tubular or funnel-shaped and typically 5-lobed with 5-lobed calyces. Fruits are dry or fleshy, containing many seeds. There are some notoriously poisonous plants in this family, such as Jimsonweed and Belladonna, as well as tobacco and important food crops—principally potato, tomato, eggplant and peppers. The showiest of the ornamentals are tropical and subtropical.

LADY-OF-THE-NIGHT (*Brunfelsia americana*), a native of the West Indies, is an erect shrub (to 8 ft.) with narrow or broad leaves (2-4 in. long). The flowers appear several times a year, in rainy periods, and are enchantingly fragrant at night. They change from white to yellow with age. Grown from seeds or cuttings in semi-shade. Variety *pubescens* blooms heavily.

NIGHT JESSAMINE (*Cestrum nocturnum*) is a West Indian shrub (to 12 ft.) with slender, drooping branches and evergreen leaves (4-8 in. long). Blooms at night, several times a year, emitting a heavy perfume. The scent and white berries are narcotic, the plant toxic to grazing animals. Fast-growing from seeds or cuttings. Day Jessamine (*C. diurnum*), with dark purple fruits, is also toxic.

YESTERDAY, TODAY AND TO-MORROW (*Brunfelsia latifolia*), from tropical America, is a shrub (2-5 ft. high) with slim branches and leaves (6-7 in. long), smooth above, slightly downy below. Flowers (spring-summer) are fragrant in daytime. They are lavender when first open, fade to white in 3 days. Slow-growing from layers; in full sun or partial shade.

PURPLE JESSAMINE (*Cestrum purpureum*), from Mexico, is an almost ever-blooming, climbing shrub (5-12 ft. high) with velvety, drooping branches and downy leaves (2½-5 in. long). Fruits are reddish-purple (to ½ in. wide) and devoured by birds, as are those of other cestrums despite their toxicity to man. Grown from seeds or cuttings in partial shade. Variety *Smithii* has rose-colored blooms.

Lady-of-the-Night

Yesterday, Today
and Tomorrow

Purple
Jessamine

Night
Jessamine

Day
Jessamine

127

ANGEL'S TRUMPET (*Datura candida*), native to southern Mexico and Central America, is a shrub (8-15 ft.) with somewhat downy leaves (to 16 in. long). Flowers (sometimes double), borne more than once a year, are strongly sweet-scented. If fruit develops, it is smooth and cylindrical. Cuttings root easily. A popular but toxic plant. Frequently misnamed *D. arborea*. Also often confused with the similar *D. suaveolens*. The peach-colored angel's trumpet (*D. mollis*) is from Ecuador. Both this species and *D. candida* bloom at least three or four times each year.

SCARLET DATURA (*Datura sanguinea*), from Peru, is a tree-like shrub (8-15 ft.) with terminal clusters of hairy leaves (to 7 in. long). Flowers nearly everblooming, are unscented. The seedpod (to 3½ in. long) is yellow and smooth. Usually grown from seeds as cuttings not easy to root. Hardier than the Angel's Trumpet; often seen in gardens in Mexico City and California. Does best in sandy soil. Seeds are narcotic. They are used in Peru to make a narcotic drink which causes mania if taken in excess. An ointment is made from the leaves.

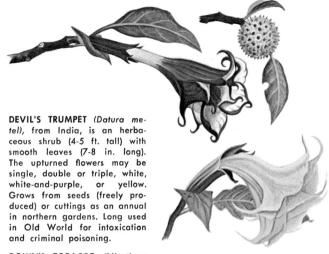

DEVIL'S TRUMPET *(Datura metel)*, from India, is an herbaceous shrub (4-5 ft. tall) with smooth leaves (7-8 in. long). The upturned flowers may be single, double or triple, white, white-and-purple, or yellow. Grows from seeds (freely produced) or cuttings as an annual in northern gardens. Long used in Old World for intoxication and criminal poisoning.

DOWNY TOBACCO *(Nicotiana tomentosa)*, a native of Brazil, is a semi-woody, downy bush (10-20 ft. high) with erect, reddish stems and handsome leaves (1½-3 ft. long), red-purple when young; in one variety, mottled yellow. The flowers, in terminal sprays, open in the evening and are very fragrant. Grows fast from seed.

PURPLE TOBACCO *(Iochroma lanceolatum)*, from Ecuador, is a soft-wooded shrub (4-8 ft. high) with hairy branches and evergreen leaves (to 6 in. long), hairy on the underside. Bears a succession of downy flowers all summer. Grows rapidly from seeds or cuttings, with plentiful moisture. Prefers sun.

CHALICE VINE *(Solandra nitida)*, native to tropical Mexico, is a woody, high-climbing vine with aerial roots and glossy, ever-green leaves (2½-4 in. long). Blooms from autumn through spring. Flowers very fragrant; are ivory white at first; turn rich yellow before falling. Grown from cuttings.

CUP FLOWER *(Nierembergia hippomanica)*, from Argentina, is a perennial herb with stiff, erect, hairy stems (to 1 ft.) and hairy leaves (to ½ in. long). Flowers are white-and-pink, or in most popular form, variety *violacea* (syn. *N. caerulea*), vio-let-blue. Grown from cuttings.

WHITE CUP *(Nierembergia re-pens)*, from Argentina, Chile and Uruguay, is a creeping plant (to 6 in. high). Stems root at joints, form dense mats. Leaves smooth (1 in. long). Flowers (summer) sometimes tinged rose or blue. Grown by stem-division in moist soil and full sun.

POTATO TREE (*Solanum macranthum*), native to Brazil, is a soft-wooded, broad-topped tree (to 30-40 ft.). Leaves (to 15 in. long) are evergreen, downy, with prominent, prickly veins beneath. Flowers (all year) increase in size and fade in color as they age, various shades present at the same time. Fruits abundant (1½-2 in. wide). Grows rapidly from seeds or cuttings; dies after 4 years. Needs partial shade.

MARRIAGE VINE (*Solanum wendlandii*), from Costa Rica, is a woody, twining vine (to 50 ft.). Leaves (to 10 in. long) deciduous in California, varying from simple to compound with 1 to 7 lobes; midrib and leafstalk have recurved prickles on underside. Blooms from summer through fall or nearly all year in tropics. Fruits ovoid (to 3 in. wide). Fast-growing (as much as 15 ft. in a season) in full sun or part shade with much moisture.

BRAZILIAN NIGHTSHADE (*Solanum seaforthianum*), probably native to Brazil, is widely cultivated in warm areas; runs wild in Australia. It is a trailing or climbing woody vine (to 10-18 ft.) with slender stems and smooth leaves (4-8 in. long), mostly divided into 3-9 deep and irregular lobes or leaflets. The flowers (white in var. *album*) and the glossy fruits hang in axillary clusters from late winter through spring. Vine is fast-growing from seeds or cuttings; begins to bloom when very young. Needs rich soil, full sun. The berries are devoured by birds but sometimes intoxicate them and have poisoned poultry and children.

MARMALADE BUSH (*Streptosolen jamesoni*), of Colombia and Ecuador, is a hairy shrub with arching branches and evergreen leaves (1½-2 in. long). Flowers in terminal clusters mainly in summer. Grows fast from cuttings in a moist soil and full sun. Short-lived.

FIGWORT FAMILY (Scrophulariaceae)

FIRECRACKER PLANT (*Russelia equisetiformis*), native to Mexico, is a bushy plant (to 4 ft.) having numerous slim, 4-angled, green, arching branches. Leaves are few and minute or scale-like. Blooms continuously. Grown from cuttings or by division. Planted in full sun as a soft hedge or deep ground cover, especially on slopes. Also used in planters or baskets. Drought-resistant but lusher if watered moderately.

CAPE FUCHSIA (*Phygelius capensis*), from South Africa, is a bushy shrub (4-10 ft. high) with smooth, herbaceous, quadrangular, purple branches and evergreen leaves (2-3 in. long). The flowers range from coral to crimson and are present in fall or nearly all year in tropics. Grown from seeds or cuttings in full sun or part shade. Drought-resistant. African natives regard it as a magic plant, affording protection from harm.

TEXAS SILVERLEAF (*Leucophyllum frutescens*), native to western Texas and northern Mexico, is a shrub (to 8 ft. high), its stems and leaves (1 in. long) coated with whitish down. Blooms in spring and may continue all summer. Propagated by cuttings and thrives in full sun in arid regions, or in humid climates on limestone soil with good drainage. Needs no care. May be lightly pruned. Mexican name is "Ceniza" (ashes).

BIGNONIA FAMILY (Bignoniaceae) includes about 100 genera and over 600 species ranging from tropical to temperate climates. They are primarily trees, shrubs and woody vines, only a very few being herbaceous plants. Leaves are usually opposite, occasionally alternate, mostly compound. Flowers are tubular or bell-shaped, generally large and colorful, in clusters. Seedpod nearly always 2-celled, splitting open, releasing flat, winged seeds (see African Tulip, *Spathodea,* p. 138). Notable exceptions are the candle trees (*Parmentiera*) with fleshy fruits, the well-known calabash trees (*Crescentia*) with fleshy, hard-shelled fruits used for maracas, and the Sausage Tree (*Kigelia,* p. 136) with curious woody fruits.

CHINESE TRUMPET CREEPER (*Campsis grandiflora*), from China and Japan, is a woody, climbing shrub (to 20-30 ft.) with deciduous, compound leaves (leaflets 1½-3 in. long). Scarlet or orange flowers, some red-striped in throat, are borne all summer. Propagated by seeds, cuttings, or rootsuckers.

SEEM TREE (*Tecomella undulata*), native from Arabia to India, is a stiff shrub or tall-trunked tree (to 30-40 ft.) with nearly evergreen, minutely hairy leaves (to 5 in. long). Blooms in spring. Grown from seeds or cuttings. It tolerates drought and is fire-resistant. Handsome wood is prized for cabinetwork.

CAT'S CLAW *(Doxantha unguis-cati)*, native from Argentina to the West Indies, is a slender-stemmed vine (to 25-40 ft.) with evergreen, compound leaves (leaflets to 3 in. long) tipped with clawlike tendrils. Flowers for 3-4 weeks in spring. Fast-growing from seeds, layers or cuttings. Thrives in full sun.

GARLIC VINE *(Pseudocalymna alliaceum)*, native to the Guianas and northern Brazil and Peru, is a high-climbing vine with glossy leaflets (to 8 in. long). Flowers are borne profusely in fall and again in spring. Vine emits garlic odor; long errone-ously known as *Cydista aequi-noctialis*. Grown from cuttings.

MANGROVE TRUMPET TREE *(Dolichandrone spathacea)*, na-tive from India through the East Indies to New Guinea, is a tree (to 45-60 ft.) with decid-uous, compound leaves (leaflets 3-6 in. long). Very fragrant flowers (in spring) open at night and fall in early morning, car-peting the ground. Grown from seeds (in slender pods to 18 in. long). Thrives on seashores and in coastal swamps. Wood used for floats and shoes. The bark yields fiber. Bark infusion used as preservative on fishing nets.

BLOOD-RED TRUMPET *(Phaedranthus buccinatorius),* from Mexico, is a climbing shrub (to 30-40 ft.). Leaves glossy, evergreen, compound (leaflets 2-4 in. long); tendrils tipped with adhesive discs. Flowers spectacular from spring to fall or all year. Grown from cuttings in full sun. Needs space.

SAUSAGE TREE *(Kigelia pinnata),* from tropical Africa, is a wide-topped tree (to 35 ft.) with evergreen leaves (to 15 in. long; leaflets 3-6 in.). Flowers (late winter or summer) open in evening, drop in morning; foul-smelling; velvety; may be orange with red spots or dark wine-red. Woody "sausages" (fruits, to 2 in. long), inedible, but abundant and curious. Tree grows slowly from seed.

JACARANDA (*Jacaranda mimosaefolia*), from Brazil, is a tree (to 50 ft.) with deciduous, feathery leaves (to 18 in. long). Lovely sprays of flowers on leafless branches in spring and a second bloom in August. Grown from seed; also grafted.

FLAME VINE (*Pyrostegia ignea*), native to Brazil, is a vine climbing by tendrils (to 40 ft.) up trees and over buildings. Leaves are evergreen, compound (leaflets 2-3 in. long). Brilliant blankets of flowers make a glorious display from late winter to spring. Grown from cuttings in full sun. Needs annual pruning.

BOWER-PLANT (*Pandorea jasminoides*), from Australia, is a woody, twining vine (20-30 ft.). Leaves evergreen, compound, glossy (leaflets 1-2 in. long). Flowers (summer-fall) white, white with pink throat, or pink. Grows fast from cuttings in sun. Similar *Podranea ricasoliana* has pink blooms striped with red, borne in large clusters.

SARITA (*Saritaea magnifica*), native to Colombia, is a handsome vine climbing by tendrils (t 30-40 ft.). The leaves (to 5 in. long) are evergreen, glossy, with recessed veins. Blooms mainly in fall-winter in Florida; summer in California. Grows fast from cuttings or air-layers in full sun. Long known as *Arrabidaea*, or *Bignonia, magnifica*.

AFRICAN TULIP TREE (*Spathodea campanulata*), from West Tropical Africa, is an erect tree (to 70 ft.) with evergreen, compound leaves (to 18 in. long; leaflets 3-4 in. long). Blooms spectacularly in late winter or early spring. Seedpods boat-shaped (to 8 in. long). Fast-growing from seeds, root-suckers or cuttings. Very susceptible to wind injury.

YELLOW ELDER (*Stenolobium stans*), a native of tropical America and the West Indies, is a bushy tree (to 20 ft.) with compound leaves (to 10 in. long; leaflets to 3½ in. long). The tree puts out a few blooms in spring; covers itself with sunny flowers in late fall. In winter, it is rather shaggy with a multitude of seedpods. Grows rapidly from seeds or cuttings.

CAPE HONEYSUCKLE (*Tecomaria capensis*), from South Africa is a semi-climbing shrub (to 25 ft.) with long, trailing or arching branches. The leaves are evergreen, compound (leaflets 1-2 in. long). Blooms mainly in fall and winter. Fast-growing from cuttings, layers or suckers in moist soil, full sun. Serves as a vine, hedge shrub, or small tree.

SILVER TRUMPET TREE (*Tabebuia argentea*), native to Paraguay, is a narrow, crooked tree (to 40 ft.). The silver-green leaves have 5-7 leaflets (3-9 in. long) and are mostly shed in late winter. In spring the tree is radiant with its masses of flowers. Seeds must be planted without delay. Growth is slow, but grafted trees bloom when only 3-4 ft. tall.

PINK TRUMPET TREE (*Tabebuia pentaphylla*), native to Central America and naturalized in the West Indies, is an erect tree (to 60-70 ft.). The deciduous leaves have 5-7 leaflets (to 6 in. long). Greatly admired for profuse flowers in spring, it is the national tree of El Salvador. Fairly fast from seed; blooms when 2 or 3 years old. Timber highly prized; resembles oak.

GLOXINIA FAMILY (Gesneriaceae)

COLUMNEA (*Columnea schiedeana*), from eastern Mexico, is a climbing, epiphytic plant with fleshy, hairy branches (to 2 ft. long). The evergreen leaves (2-5 in. long) are downy, thick and succulent, with indented rosy veins; they may be wine-red on the underside. Flowers appear from May to July. Grown from tip cuttings in hanging baskets; not in direct sun.

GLOXINIA (*Sinningia speciosa*), from Brazil, is a tuberous, nearly stemless plant with a rosette of velvety leaves (to 6 in. long). Purple-flowered in the wild, but there are many cultivated varieties and hybrids—white, or various shades of red, pink or violet; some double, some ruffled. Blooms in spring. Propagated by seeds, leaf cuttings or division. Grown in pots.

EPISCIA (*Episcia cupreata*), from Colombia, is a creeping plant (to 6 in. high), rooting at the joints and grown more for its foliage than its blooms. The leaves (2-3 in. long) of most forms are attractively embossed or "quilted" and furry; generally copper or bronze in color with silver veins; rarely glossy-green. Flowers (all year) bright red or scarlet-and-yellow. Grown from cuttings, layers, or division, in hanging baskets, in shade.

AFRICAN VIOLET (*Saintpaulia ionantha*), native to tropical East Africa, is a low herb with many downy leaves (1½-3 in. long). Flowers, which appear continuously, are typically lavender; countless varieties and hybrids display wide color range —purple, blue, red, pink, or white. Some are double. Grown from seed, leaf cuttings or division in indirect light.

TRUMPET ACHIMENES (*Achimenes longiflora*), native to Guatemala, is a hairy-stemmed plant (1-2 ft. tall) with small, tuberous rhizome. The furry leaves (1½-3 in. long) are opposite or in whorls of 3 or 4. Flowers (summer) vary from violet-blue to lavender-and-yellow, or white with yellow-and-purple throat. Propagated by stem-cuttings, offsets or division. Rhizomes are taken up and kept dry and dormant in winter.

DEVIL'S BREECHES (*Kohleria bogotensis*), from Colombia, is an erect, hairy plant (1-2 ft. high) with scaly, creeping rootstock. The leaves (2-4 in. long) are velvety and handsome. Propagated by seeds or leaf-cuttings, it is quick-growing. Often listed as *Isoloma bogotense*. A hybrid, reclining form has slenderer, bronze-green leaves and red-and-white blooms.

ACANTHUS FAMILY (Acanthaceae) embraces 180 to 200 genera and more than 2,000 species, mainly of tropical and subtropical climates; a few reaching temperate zones. They are largely herbs, subshrubs, woody shrubs, or vines; rarely trees. Leaves are opposite and simple; entire, toothed, or lobed. Flowers are tubular, usually 2-lipped, sometimes broadly flaring and 5-lobed; frequently in spikes and often cupped by leaflike, spiny or hairy bracts. The bracts may be showier than the flowers. Seedpod is 2-celled, exploding when ripe. Many members of this family are cultivated as ornamentals.

SINCLAIR'S APHELANDRA (*Aphelandra sinclairiana*), from Panama, is a shrub (6-15 ft. tall) with thin leaves (to 12 in. long) hairy beneath. In spring a few flowers at a time emerge from the showy spikes of overlapping orange-red bracts. Grown from cuttings. Pruned after blooming, for best form.

YELLOWVEIN BUSH (*Pseuderanthemum reticulatum*), from Polynesia or New Hebrides, is a bush (3-5 ft. high). Leaves (5-10 in. long) turn from yellow to green-and-yellow and lastly dark green. Blooms all year. *P. atropurpureum* has purple-and-pink leaves; mauve-and-purple blooms. Grown from cuttings.

SANGUINEA (*Megaskepasma erythrochlamys*), from Venezuela, is semi-woody, somewhat hairy, and fast-growing (to 10 ft.). Prized for its handsome, evergreen leaves (to 1 ft. long) and red bracts which are the showiest features of the terminal flower spikes. Blooms in fall. Grown from cuttings.

PHILIPPINE VIOLET (*Barleria cristata*), from India and China, is a shrub (3-10 ft. tall) with slightly hairy, evergreen leaves (to 4 in. long). Flowers may be violet, pink, or white. Fall-blooming in Florida; all year in tropics. Grown from cuttings; needs pruning. White form is naturalized in Florida.

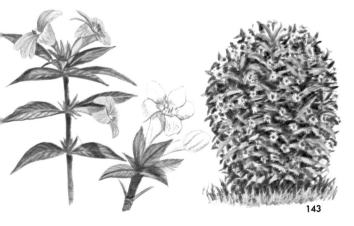

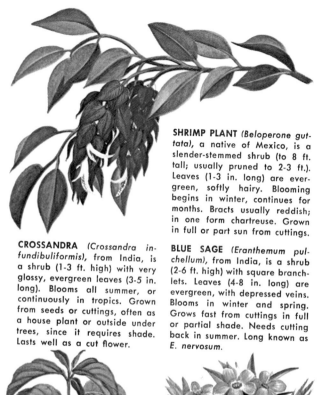

SHRIMP PLANT (*Beloperone guttata*), a native of Mexico, is a slender-stemmed shrub (to 8 ft. tall; usually pruned to 2-3 ft.). Leaves (1-3 in. long) are evergreen, softly hairy. Blooming begins in winter, continues for months. Bracts usually reddish; in one form chartreuse. Grown in full or part sun from cuttings.

CROSSANDRA (*Crossandra infundibuliformis*), from India, is a shrub (1-3 ft. high) with very glossy, evergreen leaves (3-5 in. long). Blooms all summer, or continuously in tropics. Grown from seeds or cuttings, often as a house plant or outside under trees, since it requires shade. Lasts well as a cut flower.

BLUE SAGE (*Eranthemum pulchellum*), from India, is a shrub (2-6 ft. high) with square branchlets. Leaves (4-8 in. long) are evergreen, with depressed veins. Blooms in winter and spring. Grows fast from cuttings in full or partial shade. Needs cutting back in summer. Long known as *E. nervosum*.

CARICATURE PLANT (*Graptophyllum pictum*), possibly from New Guinea, is an erect shrub (to 8-12 ft.). It is prized for its showy leaves (4-8 in. long), maroon or bronze, or more often green marbled with white, yellow, or in some forms, red. Flowers may appear any time of year. Grown from cuttings.

KING'S CROWN (*Jacobinia carnea*), native to Brazil, is a soft-stemmed shrub (3-5 ft. high). Leaves (6-10 in. long) are evergreen, downy, sometimes purplish on underside. Blooms in summer and fall. Propagated by cuttings. Needs shade, rich soil and moisture, pruning after flowering. May be espaliered.

FIRESPIKE (*Odontonema strictum*), native to Central America, is an erect, herbaceous plant (to 6-8 ft.) with evergreen leaves (3-6 in. long). Flowers open a few at a time in summer and fall; also in winter in some regions. Grows rapidly from cuttings or division in semi-shade; blooms best in full sun.

GANGES PRIMROSE *(Asystasia gangetica),* native to tropical Asia and Africa, is a trailing and climbing herb (to 4-5 ft.) with evergreen leaves (to 2½ in. long). Flowers (all year) lavender, yellow or white. Grown from seeds or cuttings.

SCARLET RUELLIA *(Ruellia macrophylla),* native to Colombia, is a handsome, soft-stemmed shrub (to 3-4 ft.) with long, downy leaves. Flowers (3 in. long) in axillary clusters in summer. Easily grown from cuttings and prized as a pot plant.

SANCHEZIA *(Sanchezia nobilis),* from Ecuador, is a shrub (to 6-12 ft.) with square branches. Evergreen leaves (to 1½ ft. long), usually variegated. Flowers (yellow with red bracts) in spring and summer. Grown from cuttings, in semi-shade.

BUSH CLOCKVINE *(Thunbergia erecta)*, from tropical Africa, is a slender-branched shrub (to 6 ft.) with smooth leaves (to 2½ in. long). Flowers (all summer) sometimes white or pale blue. Slow-growing from seeds or cuttings in sun or partial shade.

SKY VINE *(Thunbergia grandiflora)*, from India, is a stout vine (to 50 ft.) with rough leaves (to 8 in. long). Blooms nearly all year. Variety *alba* has white flowers. Grows fast from hardwood cuttings; in sun. Flowers wilt quickly when cut.

BLACK-EYED CLOCKVINE *(Thunbergia alata)*, from East Africa, is a slender vine (to 8 ft.) with velvety leaves (2-3 in. long). Blooms in late summer. Some yellow or white varieties lack the dark "eye." Grows quickly from seeds or cuttings.

MADDER FAMILY (Rubiaceae) may enfold as many as 450 genera and 5,500 species, primarily tropical. They are herbs, shrubs, vines or trees. Leaves are simple, opposite or in whorls. Flowers, borne singly or in clusters, usually have 4, 5 or 6 lobes and are mainly white or red, sometimes highly fragrant. Fruit may be a capsule, drupe or berry. Many species are important food (coffee) or drug (quinine) plants. A large number are widely cultivated ornamentals.

GARDENIA (*Gardenia jasminoides*), from China though long known as Cape Jasmine, is a shrub (to 8 ft.) with waxy, evergreen leaves (to 4 in. long). Bears fragrant, single or double flowers in spring or, in greenhouses, in winter. Grows well from cuttings or layers in acid soil. In alkaline soil must be grafted onto *G. thunbergia*.

CRIMSON IXORA (*Ixora macrothyrsa*), from the East Indies, is a shrub (to 10-12 ft.) with glossy, evergreen leaves (to 12 in. long). Blooms several times a year. Flowers used in leis in Hawaii. Grown from cuttings in acid soil; part shade for best foliage; blooms more in sun. (Recently cited as *I. casei*.)

SCARLET IXORA (*Ixora coccinea*), from southern Asia, is an erect shrub (to 8-15 ft.) with leathery leaves (2-3 in. long). Blooms all year. Grown from seeds, cuttings, or root shoots, in full sun; usually clipped as a hedge. Variety *lutea* has yellow flowers in larger clusters, and drooping branches.

RED-FLAG BUSH (*Mussaenda erythrophylla*), from West Tropical Africa, is a hairy shrub or vine (to 30 ft.; usually pruned to 6-8 ft.) with velvety leaves (3-6 in. long). Everblooming flowers not showy but flanked by a brilliant, enlarged sepal. Rare; cuttings difficult to root and seeds not produced in some areas. Grows in sun or shade.

NEEDLE-FLOWER (*Posoqueria latifolia*), from tropical America, is a shrubby tree or vine (to 18-25 ft.), the lower branches rooting where they touch ground. Leaves glossy, leathery (4-10 in. long). Flowers fragrant, abundant in spring. Yellow, round fruit is seedy but edible. Grown from seeds or layers; rich soil.

SWEET RONDELETIA (*Rondeletia odorata*), native to Cuba and Panama, is a broad shrub (6-10 ft.), with rough, leathery leaves (3-7 in. long). Blooms continuously, spring-fall. Flowers not very fragrant. Propagated by cuttings or by air-layers which require 3-4 months to root. Slow-growing.

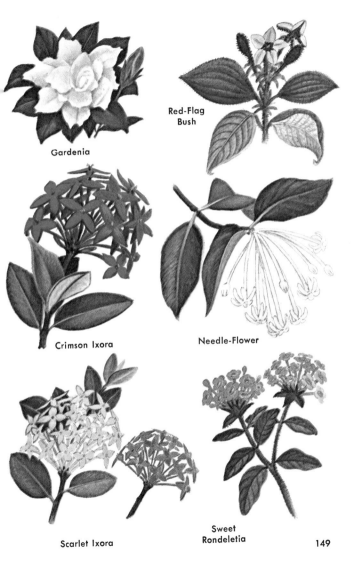

Gardenia

Red-Flag
Bush

Crimson Ixora

Needle-Flower

Scarlet Ixora

Sweet
Rondeletia

CHACONIA (*Warscewiczia coccinea*), native to Trinidad and from Mexico to Peru, is a slim tree (to 20 ft.) with evergreen leaves (to 2 ft. long). Blooms all summer. Prized for vivid sepals that enhance flower sprays. Grown from seeds in moist soil.

IVORY WOOD (*Calycophyllum spruceanum*), from Brazil, is a slender tree (to 50-70 ft.) with flaking, red-brown bark and glossy leaves (3½-7 in. long). Blooms in winter. The large white sepals outshine the small flowers. Grown from seed.

HONEYSUCKLE FAMILY
(Caprifoliaceae)

GIANT HONEYSUCKLE (*Lonicera hildebrandiana*), from Burma, is a woody, twining vine (to 80 ft.) with glossy leaves (to 8 in. long). Fragrant flowers (summer, fall) are ivory at first, then change to orange. Grows from seeds or cuttings, in some-or-part shade. Soil should be moist but well-drained. A heavy vine requiring strong support.

DAISY FAMILY (Compositae) is the largest among flowering plants and covers from 800 to 1,000 genera and 15,000 to 20,000 species distributed throughout the world. The majority are annual or perennial herbs, some are vines and a few are woody shrubs or trees. The sap may be milky. Leaves may be alternate, opposite or in whorls and are often pungent. Typical of the family is the clustering of the flowers (disk florets) in compact heads (small to large), the outer flowers (ray florets) becoming flat, strap-shaped, petal-like rays. The composite head with its encircling rays is popularly regarded as a single "flower." Seeds are usually attached to white, hairlike floss, or pappus. Many members (such as Chrysanthemums and Zinnias), highly developed, are garden favorites.

FLAT TREE DAHLIA (*Dahlia excelsa*), a native of Mexico, is a plant with several erect, unbranched, woody stems (to 20 ft.) and compound leaves (to 2½ ft. long). Blooms in late fall. Flowers single or double. Grown from seeds or cuttings.

TREE DAISY (*Montanoa hibiscifolia*), from Costa Rica and Guatemala, is a shrub or tree (to 20 ft.). Leaves entire or lobed (2-10 in. long); hairy beneath. Blooms in winter. Grown from seeds or cuttings. Dry fruits used for decoration.

TREASURE FLOWER *(Gazania rigens)*, of South Africa, is a low perennial herb with leaves (4-5 in. long) white-silky beneath. Flowers (spring or all year in some areas) open in sun, close in shade or on cloudy days. Grown from cuttings in sandy soil. Vivid ground cover in California. *G. splendens* and *G. aurantiaca* are varieties or hybrids.

MEXICAN FLAME VINE *(Senecio confusus)*, native from central to southern Mexico, is a slender, twining vine (to 25 ft.) with leathery leaves (1-4 in. long). Blooms most of year. Fast-growing from seeds, cuttings or air-layers. Does well in dry locations and full sun. May be used as a ground cover; stems rooting at joints.

CANARY CREEPER *(Senecio tamoides)*, a native of South Africa, is a climbing shrub with smooth, green stems (to 15-20 ft.). Leaves are evergreen, fleshy (to 2 in. long). Blooms profusely in fall. Fast-growing from seed or cuttings. Flourishes in partial shade but produces more flowers in full sun. Drought-resistant.

MUTISIA (*Mutisia clematis*), from Colombia and Ecuador, is a semi-woody, climbing shrub (to 20-30 ft.). Leaves evergreen, compound (the leaflets to 1½ in. long), at first downy, later smooth. Flowers all summer. Grown from seeds or cuttings in full sun. Copious nectar attracts hummingbirds. Thrives in warm locations in southern England.

TRANSVAAL DAISY (*Gerbera jamesonii*), from South Africa, is a perennial herb (to 1½ ft. high). Leaves (5-10 in. long) woolly on underside. Flowers (spring) may be single or double, white, yellow, pink, orange, red, mauve, or purple. Open in morning; close at night. Grown from seed or by division. Best in partial sun. Will stand moderate amount of foot traffic.

WEDELIA (*Wedelia trilobata*), from tropical America, is a somewhat fleshy herb (to 1 ft. high) creeping and rooting at the nodes, with glossy leaves (2-3 in. long). Blooms all year. Fast-growing from cuttings in sun or shade; is fairly salt-tolerant. A popular ground cover; may be clipped or mowed.

MORE INFORMATION

Publications of especial interest to gardeners, plant lovers generally and travelers in warm areas:

Alexander, Taylor R., et al. **Botany.** Western Publishing Co., Inc., New York. 1970.

Blatter, E. and W.S. Millard. **Some Beautiful Indian Trees.** Bombay Natural History Soc., Bombay. 2nd ed. 1954.

Bor. N.L. and M.B. Raizada. **Some Beautiful Indian Climbers and Shrubs.** Bombay Natural History Soc., Bombay. 1954.

Bruggeman, L. **Tropical Plants and Their Cultivation.** Thomas Y. Crowell Co., New York. 1957.

Camp, W.H., V.R. Boswell and J.R. Magness. **The World in Your Garden.** National Geographic Soc., Washington, D.C. 1957.

Cowen, D.V. **Flowering Trees and Shrubs in India.** Thacker & Co., Ltd., Bombay. 4th ed. 1965.

Eliovson, S. **Flowering Shrubs, Trees and Climbers from Southern Africa.** Howard Timmins. Cape Town, S. A. 1962.

Fairchild, D. **The World Was My Garden.** Charles Scribner's Sons, New York. 1941.

Graf, A.B. **Exotica 3.** Roehrs Company, Rutherford, N.J. 1969.

Greensill, T.M. **Gardening in the Tropics.** Evans Bros., Ltd., London. 1964.

Harris, T.Y. **Australian Plants for the Garden.** Angus and Robertson, Sydney. 1953.

Herbert, D.A. **Gardening in Warm Climates.** Angus and Robertson, Sydney. 1952.

Kuck, L.E. and R.C. Tongg. **Hawaiian Flowers and Flowering Trees.** Chas. E. Tuttle Co., Rutland, Vt. 1960.

McCurrach, J.C. **Palms of the World.** Harper & Row, New York. 1960.

Menninger, E. **Flowering Trees of the World:** from Tropics and Warm Climates. Hearthside Press, New York. 1962.

Menninger, E. **Flowering Vines of the World.** Hearthside Press, New York. 1970.

Morley, B.D. **Wild Flowers of the World.** G. P. Putnam's Sons, New York. 1970.

Neal, M.C. **In Gardens of Hawaii.** Bishop Museum Press, Honolulu. Rev'd ed. 1965.

O'Gorman, H. **Mexican Flowering Trees and Plants.** Ammex Asociados, Mexico City. 1961.

Shuttleworth, Floyd S., et al. **Orchids.** Western Publishing Co., Inc., New York. 1970.

van der Spuy, U. **Ornamental Shrubs and Trees for Gardens in Southern Africa.** Juta & Co., Ltd., Johannesburg. 1954.

INDEX

(See also List of Plant Families, page 8)

155

157